SOLUTIONS MANUAL
TO ACCOMPANY

PRINCIPLES OF
INSTRUMENTAL
ANALYSIS

FIFTH EDITION

SKOOG • HOLLER • NIEMAN

Douglas A. Skoog
Stanford University

F. James Holler
University of Kentucky

Timothy A. Nieman
University of Illinois at Urbana-Champaign

D1532625

BROOKS/COLE
™
THOMSON LEARNING

For permission to use material from this text contact us by:
Phone: 1-800-730-2214
Fax: 1-800-731-2215
Web: www.thomsonrights.com

Printed in the United States of America

Skoog, Holler & Nieman: Solutions Manual to accompany
Principles of Instrumental Analysis, Fifth Edition.

ISBN 0-03-002079-4

PREFACE

This manual is designed as a teaching supplement to *Principles of Instrumental Analysis*, 5th edition. It contains answers to all of the questions appearing at the end of each chapter of the text as well as detailed solutions to all of the problems.

In the solutions to problems we have tried to indicate the uncertainty associated with answers by following the significant figure convention in which the significant figures in a number are all the certain digits plus the first uncertain digit. However, we follow the practice of postponing rounding until the end of a computation in order to avoid accumulating rounding errors. Thus, intermediate results in a computation will often contain several digits that are not significant. In some solutions, we indicate our estimate of the uncertainty of a result in parentheses following the answer. Ordinarily, these numbers are our estimate of the absolute standard deviation of the result. For example, the result $3.82 (\pm 0.02) \times 10^{-3}$ indicates that our estimate of the standard deviation of the computed result is 0.02×10^{-3}.

Preparation of a solutions manual such as this that is entirely free of mistakes and errors, either typographical or computational, is unfortunately impossible. We have tried to minimize the number but are sure that users will encounter some. We would appreciate being notified of corrections so that we can incorporate them in later prints of the manual.

Douglas A. Skoog
F. James Holler
Timothy A. Nieman
August 1997

Dedication

While this book was in press, our friend, colleague, and coauthor Timothy A. Nieman of the University of Illinois at Urbana-Champaign died after a lengthy illness. His loss is a misfortune for his family, his friends, and future generations of chemistry students who might have benefited from his consummate skill as a teacher, author, research mentor, and chemist. We dedicate the fifth edition of *Principles of Instrumental Analysis* to Tim. We will miss his leadership, wisdom, counsel, and friendship.

Douglas A. Skoog
F. James Holler
August 1997

CHAPTER 1

1-1 A transducer is a device that converts information contained in chemical or physical domains into an electrical signal or the reverse. The most common input transducers convert chemical or physical information to current, voltage, or charge and the most common output transducers convert electrical signals into some numerical form.

1-2 The signal processor in a visual instrument is the human brain.

1-3 The transducer in a spectrograph is a photographic film or plate.

1-4 Smoke detectors are of two types: photodetectors and ionization detectors. The photodetectors consist of a light source such as a light-emitting diode (LED) and a photodiode to produce an electric current proportional to the intensity of the light from the LED. When smoke enters the space between the LED and the photodiode, the photocurrent decreases, which sets off an alarm. In this example, the transducer is the photodiode.

In ionization detectors, which are the typical battery-powered detectors found in homes, a small radioactive source (usually Americium) ionizes the air between a pair of electrodes. When smoke enters the space between the electrodes, the conductivity of the ionized air changes, which triggers an alarm electronically. The pair of electrodes and the air between them constitute the transducer in this type of smoke detector.

1-5 A *data domain* is one of the many modes in which data may be encoded. Examples of data domains include electrical voltage, current, and charge, frequency, time period, and digital numbers. See Section 1C for more examples.

1-6 *Analog* domains consist of electrical signals that are continuous in both magnitude and time. Example include voltage, current, charge, and power.

1-7

Output Transducer	Use
LCD readout	Indicates alphanumeric information
Computer monitor	Indicates alphanumeric information
Second hand on an electromechanical clock	Indicates time by the position of the hand
Laser printer	Produces plots of experimental data for human interpretation

1-8 A figure of merit is a number that provides quantitative information about some performance criterion for an instrument or a method.

1-9 A plot of the data is a straight line. A least-square analysis yields the equation $c_x = 0.0670\,S + 0.031$.

(a) By definition, the calibration sensitivity is the slope of the calibration curve m, or 0.0670.

(b) By definition, the analytical sensitivity $\gamma = m/s_s$ where s_s is the standard deviation of the signal. For $c_x = 2.00$ ppm, $\gamma = 0.0670/0.0094 = 7.1$. Other data computed in the same way are shown in the table at end of part (d)

(c) Substituting the blank data into Equation 1-4 gives

$$S_m = 0.031 + 3 \times 0.0079 = 0.054$$

Substitution in Equation 1-5

$$c_m = \frac{0.0547 - 0.031}{0.067} = \underline{\underline{0.35 \text{ ppm X}}}$$

(d) For 2.00 ppm X,

$$CV = (s_s/S) \times 100\% = (0.0094/0.172) \times 100\% = \underline{\underline{5.4\%}}$$

Other data computed in this same way are given in the table that follows.

c_x, ppm	γ	CV
2.00	7.1	5.4%
6.00	8.0	2.0%
10.00	8.0	1.2%
14.00	7.9	0.89%
18.00	6.1	0.88%

1-10 Let c_s = molar concentration of Cu^{2+} in standard = 0.0287 M

c_u = unknown Cu^{2+} concentration
V_s = volume of standard = 0.500 mL
V_u = volume of unknown = 25.0 mL
S_1 = signal for unknown = 23.6
S_2 = signal for unknown and standard = 37.9

Assuming signal is proportional to c_u and c_s, we have

$$S_1 = Kc_u \quad \text{or} \quad K = S_1/c_u$$

After addition of standard

$$S_2 = K\left(\frac{V_u c_u + V_s c_s}{V_u + V_s}\right)$$

Substituting for K and rearranging give

2

$$c_u = \frac{S_1 V_s c_s}{S_2 (V_u + V_s) - S_1 V_u}$$

$$= \frac{23.6 \times 0.500 \text{ mL} \times 0.0287 \text{ M}}{37.9 (0.500 \text{ mL} + 25.0 \text{ mL}) - (23.6 \times 25.0 \text{ mL})} = \underline{\underline{9.00 \times 10^{-4} \text{ M}}}$$

1-11 (a)

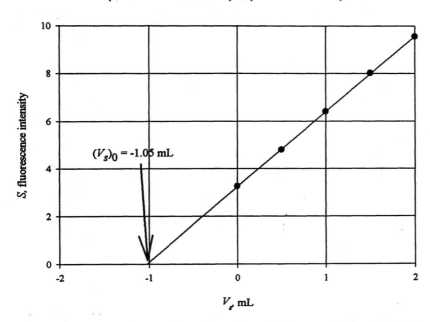

V_s, mL

(b) The extrapolated x-intercept $(V_s)_0$ from the graph in part (a) is -1.05 mL. From Example 1-3, we find the concentration of the unknown solution c_x as follows.

$$c_x = -\frac{(V_s)_0 c_s}{V_x} = -\frac{(-1.05 \text{ mL})(2.000 \text{ μg/mL})}{5.00 \text{ mL}} = \underline{\underline{0.420 \text{ μg/mL}}}$$

(c) A least-squares analysis of the data yields the following equation

$$\underline{\underline{S_1 = 3.16(\pm 0.02) V_s + 3.25(\pm 0.02)}}$$

(d)

$$c_x = \frac{b c_s}{m V_x} = \frac{(3.25)(2.000 \text{ μg/mL})}{(3.16 \text{ mL}^{-1})(5.00 \text{ mL})} = \underline{\underline{0.411 \text{ μg/mL}}}$$

(e)

$$s_c = c_x \sqrt{\left(\frac{s_{cs}}{c_s}\right)^2 + \left(\frac{s_b}{b}\right)^2 + \left(\frac{s_{V_x}}{V_x}\right)^2 + \left(\frac{s_m}{m}\right)^2}$$

Assuming that s_{cs}/c_s and s_{V_x}/V_x are small relative to the RSDs of the slope and intercept s_m/m and s_b/b, we have

$$s_c = 0.410 \text{ μg/mL} \sqrt{\left(\frac{0.02}{3.25}\right)^2 + \left(\frac{0.02}{3.16}\right)^2} = \underline{\underline{0.003 \text{ μg/mL}}}$$

3

CHAPTER 2

2-1 (a) Applying Equation 2-8 gives

$$10\,R_1/(R_1 + R_2 + R_3) = 1.0$$

$$10\,R_2/(R_1 + R_2 + R_3) = 4.0$$

$$10\,R_3/(R_1 + R_2 + R_3) = 10.0 - 1.0 - 4.0 = 5.0$$

Dividing the first equation by the second

$$R_1/R_2 = 1.0/4.0$$

Similarly,

$$R_2/R_3 = 4.0/5.0$$

Letting $\quad R_1 = \underline{50\ \Omega}, \quad R_2 = 50 \times 4.0 = \underline{200\ \Omega}$

and $\quad R_3 = 200 \times 5.0/4.0 = 250\ \Omega = \underline{200\ \Omega + 50\ \Omega}$

(b) $IR_3 = V_3 = 10 - 1.0 - 4.0 = \underline{5.0\ \text{V}}$

(c) $I = 10.0/(50 + 200 + 250) = \underline{0.020\ \text{A}}$

(d) $P = VI = 10.0 \times 0.020 = \underline{0.20\ \text{W}}$ $\quad$ (Equation $2 - 2$)

2-2 (a) $V_2 = 15 \times 500/(200 + 500 + 1000) = \underline{4.4\ \text{V}}$

(b) $P = (4.4)^2/500 = \underline{0.039\ \text{W}}$ $\quad$ (Equation $2 - 3$)

(c) Total $P = (15)^2/1700 = 0.13\ \text{W}$

% loss in $R_2 = 0.039 \times 100/0.13 = \underline{30\%}$

2-3 $V_{2,4} = 12.0 \times (2.5 + 4.0)\,10^3/(1.0 + 2.5 + 4.0)\,10^3 = 10.4\ \text{V}$

With meter in

$$\frac{1}{R_{2,4}} = \frac{1}{2.5 + 4.0} + \frac{1}{R_M} = \frac{R_M + 6.5}{6.5\,R_M}$$

$$R_{2,4} = 6.5\,R_M/(R_M + 6.5)\ \text{k}\Omega$$

4

(a) $R_{2,4} = 6.5 \times 5.0 \text{ k}\Omega / (5.00 + 6.5) \text{ k}\Omega = 2.83 \text{ k}\Omega$

$V_M = 12.0 \times 2.83 / (1.00 + 2.83) = 8.87$

rel error $= \dfrac{8.87 \text{ V} - 10.4 \text{ V}}{10.4 \text{ V}} \times 100\% = \underline{\underline{-15\%}}$

Proceeding in the same way, we obtain (b) $\underline{\underline{-1.7\%}}$ and (c) $\underline{\underline{-0.17\%}}$

2-4 Applying Equation 2 – 14, we write

(a) $-1.0\% = -\dfrac{750\,\Omega}{(R_M - 750)\,R} \times 100\%$

$R_M = 750 \times 100 - 750 \geq 74250\,\Omega$ or $\underline{\underline{\sim 74 \text{ k}\Omega}}$

(b) In the same way, $R_M \geq \underline{\underline{740 \text{ k}\Omega}}$

2-5 $1/R_{2,3} = 1/500 + 1/200$

$R_{2,3} = 143\,\Omega$

(a) $V_1 = 15.0 \times 100 / (100 + 143 + 1000) = \underline{\underline{1.21 \text{ V}}}$

$V_2 = V_3 = 15.0 \times 143 / 1243 = \underline{\underline{1.73 \text{ V}}}$

$V_4 = 15.0 \times 1000 / 1243 = \underline{\underline{12.1 \text{ V}}}$

(b) $I_1 = I_5 = 15.0 / (100 + 143 + 1000) = \underline{\underline{1.21 \times 10^{-2} \text{ A}}}$

$I_2 = 1.73 / 500 = \underline{\underline{3.5 \times 10^{-3} \text{ A}}}$

$I_3 = I_4 = 1.73 / 200 = \underline{\underline{8.6 \times 10^{-3} \text{ A}}}$

(c) $P = VI = 1.73 \times 8.6 \times 10^{-3} = \underline{\underline{1.5 \times 10^{-2} \text{ W}}}$

$V_{3,4} = 15.0 - 12.1 = \underline{\underline{2.9 \text{ V}}}$

2-6 $1/R_{1,2} = 1/2.0 \text{ k}\Omega + 1/4.0 \text{ k}\Omega \qquad 1/R_{2,3} = 1/2.0 \text{ k}\Omega + 1/1.0 \text{ k}\Omega$

$R_{1,2} = 1.33 \text{ k}\Omega \qquad\qquad\qquad R_{2,3} = 0.667 \text{ k}\Omega$

$R_T = 1.33 + 0.667 + 1.0 = 3.0 \text{ k}\Omega$

$I = 24 / (3.0 \times 1000) = 8.0 \times 10^{-3} \text{ A}$

(a) $P_{1,2} = I^2 R_{1,2} = (8.0 \times 10^{-3})^2 \times 1.33 \times 10^3 = \underline{\underline{0.085 \text{ W}}}$

(b) $I = 24/(3000) = \underline{\underline{8.0 \times 10^{-3} \text{ A}}}$

(c) $V_A = 24 \times R_A/R_T = 24 \times 1.0/3.0 = \underline{\underline{8.0 \text{ V}}}$

(d) $V_D = 24 \times R_{2,3}/R_T = 24 \times 0.667/3.0 = \underline{\underline{5.3 \text{ V}}}$

(e) $V_{5,4} = 24 - V_A = 24 - 8.0 = \underline{\underline{16 \text{ V}}}$

2-7 With the standard cell in the circuit

$$V_s = V_b \times AC/AB$$

$$1.018 = V_b \times 84.3/AB$$

With the unknown voltage V_x in the circuit,

$$V_x = V_b \times 44.3/AB$$

Dividing the third equation by the second gives

$$\frac{1.018 \text{ V}}{V_x} = \frac{84.3 \text{ cm}}{44.3 \text{ cm}}$$

$$V_x = 1.018 \text{ V} \times 44.3 \text{ cm}/84.3 \text{ cm} = \underline{\underline{0.535 \text{ V}}}$$

2-8
$$E_r = -\frac{R_s}{R_M + R_s} \times 100\%$$

$$R_s = 20\ \Omega \qquad R_M = 10\ \Omega$$

$$E_r = \frac{20\ \Omega}{10\ \Omega + 20\ \Omega} \times 100\% = -67\%$$

R_M, Ω	R_s, Ω	$E_r, \%$
10	20	-67
50	20	-29
500	20	-3.8
1.0×10^3	20	-2.0
1.0×10^4	20	-0.20

2-9
$$E_r = -\frac{R_{std}}{R_L + R_{std}} \times 100\%$$

$$R_{std} = 1\ \Omega \qquad R_L = 1\ \Omega$$

6

$$E_r = -\frac{1\,\Omega}{1\,\Omega + 1\,\Omega} \times 100\% = -50\%$$

$R_L,\,\Omega$	$R_{std},\,\Omega$	$E_r,\,\%$
1.0	1	−50
10	1	−9.1
100	1	−0.99
1000	1	−0.10

2-10 (a) $R_s = E/I = 1.00\,\text{V}/(50\,\mu\text{A} \times 10^{-6}\,\text{A}/\mu\text{A}) = 20000\text{ ohms}$ or <u>20 kΩ</u>

(b) $-1\% = -\dfrac{20\,\text{k}\Omega}{R_M - 20\,\text{k}\Omega} \times 100\%$ (Equation 2 − 14)

$R_M = (20 \times 100 - 20)\,\text{k}\Omega = 1980\,\text{k}\Omega$ or <u>~ 2 MΩ</u>

2-11 $I_1 = 90/(20 + 5000) = 1.793 \times 10^{-2}\,\text{A}$

$I_2 = 90/(40 + 5000) = 1.786 \times 10^{-2}$

current change $= -0.007 \times 10^{-2}\,\text{A}$

% change $= (-0.007 \times 10^{-2})/(1.793 \times 10^{-2}) \times 100\% = \underline{-0.4\%}$

2-12 $I_1 = 9.0/520 = 1.731 \times 10^{-2}\,\text{A}$

$I_2 = 9.0/540 = 1.667 \times 10^{-2}\,\text{A}$

current change $= -0.064 \times 10^{-2}\,\text{A}$

% change $= (-0.064 \times 10^{-2})/(1.731 \times 10^{-2}) \times 100\% = \underline{-3.7\%}$

2-13 $i = I_{init}\,e^{-t/RC}$ (Equation 2 − 30)

$RC = 10 \times 10^{6} \times 0.2 \times 10^{-6} = 2.00$ $I_{init} = 24/(10 \times 10^{6})$

$i = 2.4 \times 10^{-6}\,e^{-t/2.00}\,\text{A}$ or $2.4\,e^{-t/2.0}\,\mu\text{A}$

$t,\,\text{s}$	$i,\,\mu\text{A}$	$t,\,\text{s}$	$i,\,\mu\text{A}$
0.00	2.40	1.0	1.4
0.010	2.39	10	0.0162
0.10	2.28		

2-14 $v_c = V_c e^{-t/RC}$ (Equation 2 − 35)

$v_c/V_c = 1.00/100$

$0.0100 = e^{-t/R \times 0.015 \times 10^{-6}}$

$\ln\ 0.0100 = -4.61 = -t/1.5 \times 10^{-8}\,R$

$t = 4.61 \times 1.5 \times 10^{-8}\,R = 6.90 \times 10^{-8}\,R$

(a) When $R = 10\,\text{M}\,\Omega$ or $10 \times 10^{6}\,\Omega$, $t = \underline{\underline{0.69\ \text{s}}}$

(b) Similarly, $t = \underline{\underline{0.069\ \text{s}}}$

(c) Similarly, $t = \underline{\underline{6.9 \times 10^{-5}\ \text{s}}}$

2-15 (a) $RC = 0.015 \times 10^{-6} \times 10 \times 10^{6} = \underline{0.15\ \text{s}}$

(b) $RC = \underline{\underline{0.015\ \text{s}}}$

(c) $RC = \underline{\underline{1.5 \times 10^{-5}\ \text{s}}}$

2-16 (a) $RC = 50 \times 10^{3} \times 0.035 \times 10^{-6} = 1.75 \times 10^{-3}\ \text{s}$ or $\underline{\underline{1.75\ \text{ms}}}$

(b) $I_{\text{init}} = 25/50 \times 10^{3} = 5.0 \times 10^{-4}\ \text{A}$ or $\underline{\underline{5.0 \times 10^{2}\ \mu\text{A}}}$

t, ms	$i = 500\,e^{-t/1.75}$	$v_R = 50 \times 10^{3} \times i$	$v_c = (25 - v_R)$
0	500 μA	25 V	0.0 V
1	282	14	11
2	159	8.0	17
3	90	4.5	20
4	51	2.5	22
5	29	1.4	24
10	1.6	0.08	24.9

(c) $i = \dfrac{-V_c}{R}e^{-t/1.75} = \dfrac{-24.9}{50 \times 10^{3}} \times 10^{6}\,e^{-0/1.75} = -498\ \mu\text{A}$

$v_R = -498 \times 50 \times 10^{3} = -24.9$ $v_c = -v_R = 24.9$

8

t, ms	$i = -498\,e^{-t/1.75}$	$v_R = 50 \times 10^3 \times i$	$v_c = -v_R$
0	$-498\ \mu A$	-24.9 V	24.9 V
1	-281	-14.1	14.1
2	-159	-7.9	7.9
3	-90	-4.5	4.5
4	-51	-2.5	2.5
5	-29	-1.4	1.4
10	-1.6	-0.08	0.08

2-17 (a) $RC = 20 \times 10^6 \times 0.050 \times 10^{-6} = \underline{\underline{1.00\ \text{s}}}$

(b) $I_{\text{init}} = 15/(20 \times 10^6) = 7.5 \times 10^{-7}\ \text{A} \quad \text{or} \quad 0.75\ \mu A$

$\quad\quad i = 0.750\,e^{-t/1.00} \quad \text{at} \quad t = 0, \quad i = 0.750\,e^{-0/1.00} = 0.750\ \mu A$

$\quad\quad v_R = 0.750 \times 10^{-6} \times 20 \times 10^6 = 15\ \text{V}$

$\quad\quad v_c = 0.00$

t, ms	$i = 0.75\,e^{-t/1.00}$	$v_R = i \times R$	$v_c = 15.0 - v_R$
0	$0.75\ \mu A$	15.0 V	0.0 V
1	0.28	5.5	9.5
2	0.10	2.0	13.0
3	3.7×10^{-2}	0.75	14.2
4	1.4×10^{-2}	0.27	14.7
5	5.0×10^{-3}	0.10	14.9
10	3.0×10^{-5}	0.00	15.0

(c) $i = \dfrac{-15.0}{20 \times 10^6}\,e^{-t/1.00} \quad \text{at} \quad t = 0, \quad i = 0.75 \times 10^{-6}\ \text{A} \quad \text{or} \quad 0.75\ \mu A$

t, ms	$i = -0.75\,e^{-t/1.00}$	$v_R = i \times R$	$v_c = -v_R$
0	$-0.75\ \mu A$	-15.0 V	15.0 V
1	-0.28	-5.5	5.5
2	-0.10	-2.0	2.0
3	-3.7×10^{-2}	-0.75	0.75
4	-1.4×10^{-2}	-0.27	0.27
5	-5.0×10^{-3}	-0.10	0.10
10	-3.4×10^{-5}	0.00	0.00

2-18 (a) $X_c = 1/2\pi fC = 1/(2\pi \times 1 \times 0.033 \times 10^{-6}) = 4.8 \times 10^6\ \Omega$

$$Z = \sqrt{(4.8 \times 10^6)^2 + (20,000)^2} = 4.8 \times 10^6\ \Omega$$

$$\phi = -\arctan(X_c/R) = \arctan(4.8 \times 10^6 \times 20,000) = -90\ \text{deg}$$

Following this same procedure, we find

	X_c, Ω	Z, Ω	ϕ, deg
(a)	4.8×10^6	4.8×10^6	-90
(b)	4.8×10^3	2.1×10^4	-13.6
(c)	4.8	2.0×10^4	0.0
(d)	4.8×10^6	4.8×10^3	-90
(e)	4.8×10^3	4.8×10^3	-87.6
(f)	4.8	200	-1.4
(g)	4.8×10^5	4.8×10^5	-90
(h)	4.8×10^2	2.1×10^3	-13.6
(i)	4.8	2.0×10^3	0.0

2-19 Equation 2-49 is the equation in the right-hand column on page 36. The equation number is missing in the first printing of the book. Let us rewrite Equation 2-49 in the form

$$y = \frac{(V_p)_o}{(V_p)_i} = \frac{1}{\sqrt{(2\pi fRC)^2 + 1}}$$

$$y^2\,(2\pi fRC)^2 + y^2 = 1$$

$$f = \frac{1}{2\pi RC}\sqrt{\frac{1}{y^2}-1}$$

$$= \frac{1}{2\pi \times 0.015 \times 10^{-6} \times 2.5 \times 10^5}\sqrt{\frac{1}{y^2}-1} = 42.4\sqrt{\frac{1}{y^2}-1}$$

$(V_p)_o/(V_p)_i$	f	$(V_p)_o/(V_p)_i$	f
0.01	4.2×10^3	0.60	57
0.10	4.2×10^2	0.80	32
0.20	2.1×10^2	0.90	21
0.40	97	0.99	61

2-20 By dividing the numerator and denominator of the right side of Equation 2-48 by R, we obtain

$$y = \frac{(V_p)_o}{(V_p)_i} = \frac{1}{\sqrt{1+(1/2\pi fRC)^2}}$$

Squaring this equation yields

$$y^2 + y^2/(2\pi fRC)^2 = 1$$

$$2\pi fRC = \sqrt{y^2/(1-y^2)}$$

$$f = \sqrt{\frac{y^2/(1-y^2)}{2\pi RC}} = \sqrt{\frac{y^2(1-y^2)}{2\pi \times 5.0 \times 10^5 \times 100 \times 10^{-12}}}$$

$$= 1.59 \times 10^3 \sqrt{y^2/(1-y^2)}$$

When $(V_p)_o/(V_p)_i = y = 0.01$

$$f = 1.59 \times 10^3 \sqrt{(0.01)^2/(1-0.01)^2} = \underline{1.6 \times 10^1\ \text{Hz}}$$

The data that follow were obtained in this same way.

$(V_p)_o/(V_p)_i$	f	$(V_p)_o/(V_p)_i$	f
0.01	1.6×10^1	0.6	1.2×10^3
0.10	1.6×10^2	0.8	2.1×10^3
0.20	3.2×10^2	0.9	3.3×10^3
0.40	7.0×10^2	0.99	1.1×10^4

CHAPTER 3

3-1 **(a)**

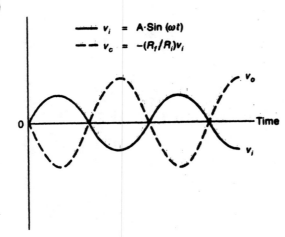

$v_i = A \cdot \text{Sin} (\omega t)$
$v_c = -(R_f/R_i)v_i$

(b)

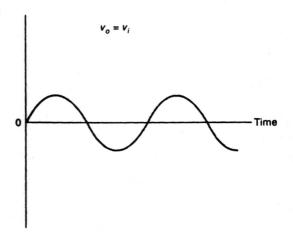

$v_o = v_i$

(c)

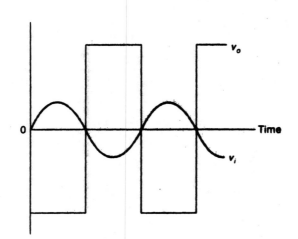

(d)

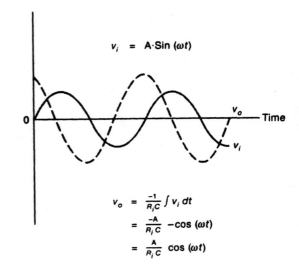

$v_i = A \cdot \text{Sin} (\omega t)$

$$v_o = \frac{-1}{R_i C} \int v_i \, dt$$
$$= \frac{-A}{R_i C} - \cos (\omega t)$$
$$= \frac{A}{R_i C} \cos (\omega t)$$

(e)

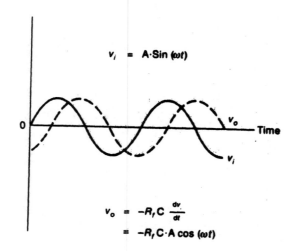

$v_i = A \cdot \text{Sin} (\omega t)$

$$v_o = -R_f C \frac{dv_i}{dt}$$
$$= -R_f C \cdot A \cos (\omega t)$$

12

3-2 (a) The exact equation for op amp gain is given near the top of the left-hand column of page 57 as

$$\frac{v_i - \left(v_+ - \frac{v_o}{A}\right)}{R_i} = \frac{\left(v_+ - \frac{v_o}{A}\right) - v_o}{R_f}$$

Since $v_+ \approx 0$, we may write

$$\frac{v_i + \frac{v_o}{A}}{R_i} = \frac{-\frac{v_o}{A} - v_o}{R_f}$$

Solving for v_o, we obtain

$$v_o = -\frac{v_i R_f}{\frac{R_f - R_i}{A} + R_i}$$

Substituting values for the variables, we calculate

$$v_o = -\frac{(0.910\,\text{mV})(30.0\,\text{k}\Omega)}{\frac{30.0\,\text{k}\Omega - 1.00\,\text{k}\Omega}{200} + 1.00\,\text{k}\Omega} = \underline{\underline{-23.8\,\text{mV}}}$$

Equation 3-7 yields 27.3 mV.

(b) $I_i = (V_i - v_s)/R_i$

But $v = 0$

$I_i = 0.910 \times 10^{-3}\,\text{V}/1.00 \times 10^3\,\Omega$

$= \underline{\underline{9.10 \times 10^{-7}\,\text{A} \quad \text{or} \quad 0.910\,\mu\text{A}}}$

(c) $\underline{\underline{I_f = I_i = 0.910\,\mu\text{A}}}$

3-3 The rise time t_r for an op amp is given by Equation 3-8.

$$t_r = \frac{1}{3\,\Delta f} = \frac{1}{3.50\,\text{MHz}} = 6.7 \times 10^{-9}\,\text{s} = \underline{\underline{6.7\,\text{ns}}}$$

Although no voltage change is given in the problem, we may assume a typical value of 10 V and calculate the slew rate as

$$\text{slew rate} = \frac{\Delta v}{\Delta f} = \frac{10\,\text{V}}{6.7\,\text{ns}} = 1.5 \times 10^9\,\text{V/s} = \underline{\underline{1500\,\text{V/}\mu\text{s}}}$$

3-4 $v_0 = -v_i \times 40.0/2.00 = -2.00\,v_i \qquad$ (Equation 3 – 7)

The more exact expression is given in the solution to Problem 3-2a as

$$(v_o)_e \;=\; -\frac{v_i R_f}{\dfrac{R_f - R_i}{A} + R_i} \;=\; -v_i\left(\dfrac{R_f}{\dfrac{R_f - R_i}{A} + R_i}\right)$$

$$=\; -v_i\left(\dfrac{40.0 \text{ M}\Omega}{\dfrac{40.0 \text{ M}\Omega - 2.00 \text{ M}\Omega}{5 \times 10^4} + 2.00 \text{ m}\Omega}\right) \;=\; -19.992\,v_i$$

The value give by Equation 3-7 (not 3-6) is

$$(v_o)_a \;=\; -v_i\left(\dfrac{R_f}{R_i}\right) \;=\; -v_i\left(\dfrac{40.0 \text{ m}\Omega}{2.00 \text{ M}\Omega}\right) \;=\; -20.000\,v_i$$

$$\text{rel}\quad \text{error} \;=\; \frac{-19.992\,v_i - (-20.000\,v_i)}{-19.992\,v_i} \times 100\% \;=\; \underline{\underline{+0.04\%}}$$

3-5

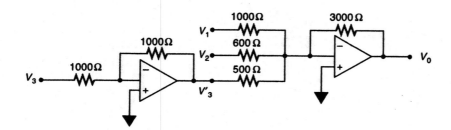

$$V_0 \;=\; -R_f\left(\frac{V_1}{R_1} + \frac{V_2}{R_2} + \frac{V_3}{R_f}\right) \qquad V_3' \;=\; -\frac{1000}{1000}\,V_3 \;=\; -V_3$$

$$V_0 \;=\; -3000\left(\frac{V_1}{1000} + \frac{V_2}{600} + \frac{V_3}{500}\right) \;=\; \underline{\underline{-3V_1 - 5V_2 + 6V_3}}$$

3-6

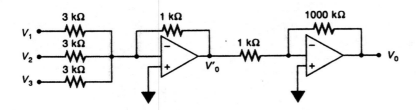

$$V_0' \;=\; -1 \times \left(\frac{V_1}{3} + \frac{V_2}{3} + \frac{V_3}{3}\right)$$

$$V_0 = -V_0' \times \frac{1000}{1} = \frac{V_1 + V_2 + V_3}{3} \times 1000$$

3-7

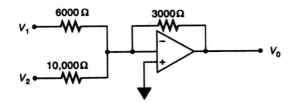

$$V_0 = -R_f\left(\frac{V_1}{R_1} + \frac{V_2}{R_3}\right)$$

$$= -3000\left(\frac{V_1}{6000} + \frac{V_2}{10000}\right) = \underline{\underline{-(0.500\ V_1 + 0.3003 V_2)}}$$

3-8 $R_f = 1.00\ k\Omega$ and $R_1 = 250\ \Omega$

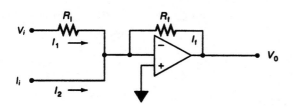

$$I_1 + I_i = I_f$$

$$\frac{V_i}{R_1} + I_2 \approx -\frac{V_0}{R_f}$$

$$-V_0 = \frac{V_i R_f}{R_1} + I_i R_f$$

Let $R_f = 1.00 \times 10^3\ \Omega$ and $R_1 = 250\ \Omega$. Then

$$-V_0 = \frac{V_i \times 1.00 \times 10^3}{250} + 1.00 \times 10^3\ I_i = \underline{\underline{4\ V_i + 1.00 \times 10^3\ I_i}}$$

3-9 (a) Let V_x be the output from the first operational amplifier,

$$V_x = \frac{V_1 R_{f1}}{R_1} - \frac{V_2 R_{f1}}{R_2}$$

and

$$V_0 = -\frac{V_x R_{f2}}{R_4} = +\frac{V_1 R_{f1} R_{f2}}{R_1 R_4} + \frac{V_2 R_{f1} R_{f2}}{R_2 R_4} - \frac{V_3 R_{f2}}{R_3}$$

(b)
$$V_0 = \frac{200 \times 400}{200 \times 400} V_1 + \frac{200 \times 400}{50 \times 400} V_2 - \frac{400}{10} V_3$$

$$= \underline{\underline{V_1 + 4 V_2 - 40 V_3}}$$

3-10 The output voltage V_x from the first operational amlifier is

$$-V_x = \frac{15 V_1}{3} + \frac{15 V_2}{5} = 5 V_1 + 3 V_2$$

Then

$$V_0 = -\frac{V_x \times 12}{6} - \frac{V_3 \times 12}{4} - \frac{V_4 \times 12}{6}$$

$$= \underline{\underline{10 V_1 + 6 V_2 - 3 V_3 - 2 V_4}}$$

3-11 Operation amplifier 1 is an integrator configuration whose output voltage is given by Equation 3-22. That is,

$$(v_o)_1 = -\frac{1}{R_i C_f} \int_{t_1=0}^{t_2=t} v_i \, dt = \left(\frac{-v_i}{R_i C_f}\right) t$$

Operation amplifier 2 is in a differentiating configuration where Equation 3-19 applies. That is,

$$(v_o)_2 = -R_f C_i \frac{d(v_o)_1}{dt}$$

$$= -R_f C_i \frac{d}{dt}\left(\frac{-v_i}{R_i C_f} t\right) = \underline{\underline{\frac{R_f C_i}{R_i C_f} v_i}}$$

In the sketch that follows, it is assume that $(R_f C_i)/(R_i C_f) > 1$

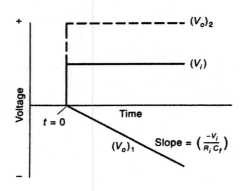

3-12 In an operational amplifier circuit, $v_- = v_+$, (Equation 3-3). Thus,

$$V_i = v_+ = v_- = IR_1$$

$$\frac{V_o}{V_i} = \frac{I(R_1 + R_2)}{IR_1} = \left(\frac{R_1 + R_2}{R_1}\right)$$

$$V_o = \left(\frac{R_1 + R_2}{R_1}\right) V_i$$

3-13 $V_o = -Ix$ and $v_- = v_+ = 0$

$$V_i = I(R - x)$$

$$\frac{V_o}{V_i} = \frac{-Ix}{I(R - x)} = -\frac{x}{R - x}$$

$$V_o = -\left(\frac{x}{R - x}\right) V_i$$

3-14 $I_i = I_1 + I_2 = I_f$

$$\frac{V_1}{20 \times 10^6} + \frac{V_2}{5.0 \times 10^6} = -C\frac{dV_o}{dt} = -0.010 \times 10^{-6}\frac{dV_o}{dt}$$

$$\frac{dV_o}{dt} = -\left(\frac{V_1}{0.20} + \frac{V_2}{0.05}\right)$$

$$V_o = -(5\,V_1 + 20\,V_2)\int_o^t dt$$

3-15 This circuit is analogous to that shown in Figure 3-11, page 63, with the added stipulations that

$$R_1 = R_{k1} = R_2 = R_{k2}$$

Equation 3-15 then applies and we may write

$$V_o = \frac{R_k}{R_i}(V_2 - V_1) = V_2 - V_1$$

3-16 $1.02 = V_o \times \overline{AC}/\overline{AB} = 3.00 \times \overline{AC}/100$

$$\overline{AC} = 100\,\text{cm} \times 1.02/3.00 = \underline{34.0\,\text{cm}}$$

Here, $(v_o)_1 = -\dfrac{1}{10 \times 10^6 \times 0.10 \times 10^{-6}} \displaystyle\int_0^t v_1 dt = -1.0 \displaystyle\int_0^t v_1 dt$ (see Figure 3 – 14c)

Similarly,

$$(v_o)_2 = -1.0 \int_0^t v_2 dt$$

Then

$$v_o = -20 \left[\frac{(v_o)_1}{5.0} + \frac{(v_o)_2}{4.0} \right] = -4.0 (v_o)_1 - 5 (v_o)_2$$

and

$$v_o = +4.0 \int_0^t v_1 dt + 5.0 \int_0^t v_2 dt$$

3-17

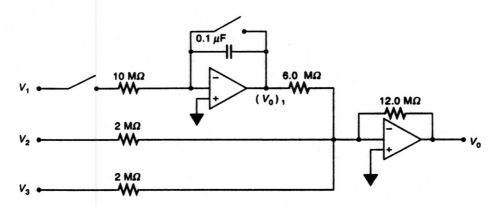

Here,

$$(v_o)_1 = -\frac{1}{10 \times 10^6 \times 0.1 \times 10^{-6}} \int_0^t v_1 dt = -1.0 \int_0^t v_1 dt$$

$$v_o = -12.0 \left[\frac{(v_o)_1}{6} + \frac{v_2}{2} + \frac{v_3}{2} \right] = -2 (v_o)_1 - 6 (v_2 + v_3)$$

$$= +2.0 \int_0^t v_1 dt - 6 (v_2 + v_3)$$

3-18 $v_o = -\dfrac{1}{R_i C_i} \displaystyle\int_0^t v_1 dt = -\dfrac{1}{2 \times 10^6 \times 0.25 \times 10^{-6}} \displaystyle\int_0^t 4.0\, dt$

$$= -2 \int_0^t 4.0\, dt = -8.0\, t$$

Substituting into this equation gives

18

$\dfrac{t}{v_o}$	1 s	3 s	5 s	7 s
	−8 mV	−24 mV	−40 mV	−56 mV

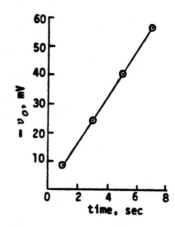

CHAPTER 4

4-1 (a) $2^4 = 16$ $24 - 16 = 8$

$2^3 = 8$ $8 - 8 = 0$

binary	1	1	0	0	0
	$1 \cdot 2^4 +$	$1 \cdot 2^3 +$	$0 \cdot 2^2 +$	$0 \cdot 2^1 +$	$0 \cdot 2^0$

(b) $2^6 = 64$ $79 - 64 = 15$

$2^3 = 8$ $15 - 8 = 7$

$2^2 = 4$ $7 - 4 = 3$

$2^1 = 2$ $3 - 2 = 1$

$2^0 = 1$ $1 - 1 = 0$

binary	1	0	0	1	1	1	1
	$1 \cdot 2^6 +$	$0 \cdot 2^5 +$	$0 \cdot 2^4 +$	$1 \cdot 2^3 +$	$1 \cdot 2^2 +$	$1 \cdot 2^1 +$	$1 \cdot 2^0$

In similar fashion we find

(c) $136_{10} = 10001000_2$

(d) $581_{10} = 1001000101_2$

4-2 (a) $101_2 = 1 \cdot 2^2 + 0 \cdot 2^1 + 1 \cdot 2^0$

$= 4 + 0 + 1 = \underline{\underline{5_{10}}}$

(b) $10101_2 = 1 \cdot 2^4 + 0 \cdot 2^3 + 1 \cdot 2^2 + 0 \cdot 2^1 + 1 \cdot 2^0$

$= 16 + 0 + 4 + 0 + 1 = \underline{\underline{21_{10}}}$

In similar fashion we find

(c) 11100010_2 = $\underline{\underline{226_{10}}}$

(d) 1101001001_2 = $\underline{\underline{841_{10}}}$

4-3 We assume that the maximum digitization error is ± 1 LSB.

(a) 2^8 = 256   10 V / 256 = $\underline{\underline{0.039 \text{ V}}}$

(b) 2^{12} = 4096   10 V / 4096 = $\underline{\underline{0.0024 \text{ V}}}$

(c) 2^{16} = 65,536   10 V / 65,536 = $\underline{\underline{0.00015 \text{ V}}}$

4-4 If the measurements are made with *exactly* the same converters as in Problem 4-3, the answers are identical. That is the input ranges of the converter are still 10 V full scale, then 1 V is 1/10 of full scale, so for converter (a), this represents 1/10 of the range, or 256/10 = 26. Thus, 1 V / 26 = $\underline{\underline{0.038 \text{ V}}}$. The same is true for all three converters. If, however, the 1 V signal is scaled to the full range of the converter using an amplifier, then

(a) 2^8 = 256   1 V / 256 = $\underline{\underline{0.0039 \text{ V}}}$

(b) 2^{12} = 4096   1 V / 4096 = $\underline{\underline{0.00024 \text{ V}}}$

(c) 2^{16} = 65,536   1 V / 65,536 = $\underline{\underline{0.000015 \text{ V}}}$

4-5 As suggested by the answer to Problem 4-4, we shall assume that by "same ADC" we mean the same number of bits and that full scale is 10 V in both cases. Thus we divide the two expressions for the maximum % error to obtain 10 V / 1 V = 10.

4-6 (a) 20 s / 20 points = 1 s / point

$$\frac{1}{1 \text{ s / point}} = 1 \text{ point / s} \quad \text{or} \quad \underline{\underline{1 \text{ Hz}}}$$

(b) 1 s / 20 points = 0.05 s / point

$$\frac{1}{0.05 \text{ s / point}} = 20 \text{ points / s} = \underline{\underline{20 \text{ Hz}}}$$

4-7 Conversion frequency $= \dfrac{1}{8 \text{ μs}} = \dfrac{1}{8 \times 10^{-6} \text{ s}} = \underline{\underline{125 \text{ kHz}}}$

According to the Nyquist criterion, the maximum signal frequency should be half the conversion frequency, or

20

$$f_{max} = \frac{1}{2} \times 125 \text{ kHz} = \underline{\underline{62.5 \text{ kHz}}}$$

4-8 (a) Number accessible memory locations $= 2^{36} = 68,719,476,736$ or nearly 69 gigabytes (69 GB).

(b) Number of possible instructions $= 2^{64} = 1.84 \times 10^{19}$ instructions.

CHAPTER 5

5-1 Frequency dependent: flicker and environmental noise.
Frequency independent: thermal and shot noise.

5-2 (a) Thermal noise.

(b) Certain types of environmental noise.

(c) Thermal and shot noise.

5-3 10^4 to 10^5 and 10^6 to 10^7 Hz. Environmental noise is at a minimum in these regions (see Figure 5-3).

5-4 At the high impedance of a glass electrode, shielding is vital to prevent currents induced from power lines from being amplified and disturbing the output.

5-5 (a) High-pass filters are used in order to remove low frequency flicker noise from high frequency analytical signals.

(b) Low-pass filters are used to remove high frequency noise from dc analytical signals.

5-6 We estimate the maximum and the minimum in the recorded signal (0.9×10^{-15} μA) to be 1.5×10^{-15} and 0.4×10^{-15} μA. The standard deviation of the signal is estimated to be one fifth of the difference (page 100) or 0.22×10^{-15} μA. Thus,

$$S/N = \frac{0.9 \times 10^{-15} \text{ μA}}{0.22 \times 10^{-15} \text{ μA}} = \underline{\underline{4}}$$

5-7 (a) The mean for the data is $\bar{x} = 1.003$.

The standard deviation is $s = 2.80 \times 10^{-3}$ (Equation a1-9, page A-6).

$$S/N = 1.003/2.80 \times 10^{-3} = \underline{\underline{358}}$$

(b) $\dfrac{S}{N} = \dfrac{S_n}{N_n}\sqrt{n}$ (Equation 5 – 11)

For the nine measurements

$$358 = \frac{S_n}{N_n}\sqrt{9}$$

For S/N to be 500, will require n_x measurements. That is

$$500 = \frac{S_n}{N_n}\sqrt{n_x}$$

Dividing the second equation by the first gives after squaring and rearranging

$$n_x = \left(\frac{500}{358} \times 3\right)^2 = 17.6 = \underline{\underline{18 \text{ measurements}}}$$

5-8 Proceeding as in Solution 5-7 we obtain

(a) $\bar{x} = \underline{1.435}$ and $s = \underline{0.271}$

$S/N = 1.435/0.271 = \underline{\underline{5.3}}$

(b)
$$n_x = \left(\frac{10}{5.3} \times \sqrt{8}\right)^2 = 28.5 = \underline{\underline{29 \text{ measurements}}}$$

5-9 $V_{rms} = \sqrt{4\,kTR\Delta f} = \sqrt{4 \times 1.38 \times 10^{-23} \times 298 \times 1 \times 10^6 \times 1 \times 10^6}$

$$= \underline{\underline{1.28 \times 10^{-4} \text{ V}}}$$

$$\frac{(V_{rms})_2}{(V_{rms})_1} = \frac{\sqrt{\Delta f_1}}{\sqrt{\Delta f_2}}$$

$$(V_{rms})_2 = (V_{rms})_1 \times \frac{\sqrt{1.0 \times 10^2}}{\sqrt{1 \times 10^6}} = \underline{\underline{\frac{(V_{rms})_1}{100}}}$$

5-10 $\dfrac{S}{N} = \sqrt{1}\,\dfrac{S_x}{N_x} = \underline{\underline{4.3}}$

$\dfrac{S}{N} = \sqrt{n}\,\dfrac{S_x}{N_x} = \underline{\underline{43}}$

Dividing the second equation by the first gives

$$\frac{\sqrt{n}}{\sqrt{1}} = \frac{43}{4.3} = \underline{\underline{10}}$$

$$n = 10^2 = \underline{\underline{100}}$$

5-11

$$\frac{(S/N)_{50}}{(S/N)_1} = \frac{\sqrt{50}}{\sqrt{1}} = \underline{\underline{7.1}}$$

$$\frac{(S/N)_{200}}{(S/N)_1} = \frac{\sqrt{200}}{\sqrt{1}} = \underline{\underline{14.1}}$$

5-12 The magnitudes of the signals and the noise on the spectra in Figure 5-15 may be estimated directly from the graphs. The results from our estimates are listed in the table below. Baselines for spectra A and D are taken from the flat regions on the right side of the figure. Noise is calculated from one fifth of the peak-to-peak excursions of the signal.

	A_{255}	A_{425}	A_b (peak)	A_b(valley)	A_b(mean)
Spectrum A	0.550	0.580	0.080	-0.082	0.001
Spectrum B	1.125	1.150	0.620	0.581	0 .600

	S_{255}	S_{425}	$N = A_b/\text{peak}) - A_b/\text{valley})/5$	$(S/N)_{255}$	$(S/N)_{425}$
Spectrum A	0.549	0.579	0.0324	17	18
Spectrum B	0.525	0.550	0.0078	67	70

Note that the difference in S/N for the two peaks is due only to the difference in the peak heights.

5-13 We estimate the peak widths at half maximum for the two peaks to be

$\dfrac{\text{FWHM}_{255}}{50 \text{ nm}}$	$\dfrac{\text{FWHM}_{425}}{100 \text{ nm}}$

Thus, the smooth widths for the two peaks should be no more than twice these widths, or 100 nm for the peak at 255 nm and 200 nm for the peak at 425 nm. Since we do not know the number of data points in the spectra we cannot determine the smooth widths in terms of data points. However, if we assume that each spectrum is 1000 data points wide, then we have 500 nm/1000 points = 0.5 nm/pt. For the two peaks, the smooth widths should be

$$100 \text{ nm} / 0.5 \text{ nm/pt} = \underline{\underline{200 \text{ points}}} \quad \text{and} \quad 200 \text{ nm} / 0.5 \text{ nm/pt} = \underline{\underline{400 \text{ points}}}$$

CHAPTER 6

6-1 (a) Coherent radiation is radiation that is made up of wave trains having identical frequencies or sets of frequencies and phase relationships that are constant with time.

(b) Dispersion in a transparent material is its variation in refractive index as a function of wavelength.

(c) Anomalous dispersion is the sharp change in refractive index of a substance in a wavelength region where absorption is occurring.

(d) The work function of a substance is a constant that measures the energy required to remove an electron from the surface of the substance.

(e) The photoelectric effect involves the emission of electrons from the surface of a substance brought about by a beam of radiation.

(f) The ground state of a molecule is its lowest energy state.

(g) Electronic excitation is the process by which electrons in a substance are promoted from their ground state orbitals to higher electronic orbitals by absorption of energy.

(h) Blackbody radiation is the continuous radiation emitted by a solid when it is heated.

(i) Fluorescence is a type of emission which is brought about by irradiating atoms, ions, or molecules with electromagnetic radiation. Fluorescence takes place over a period of 10^{-5} s or less.

(j) Phosphorescence is a type of emission, which is brought about by irradiating a chemical substance with electromagnetic radiation. Phosphorescence continues for a longer time than fluorescence ($> 10^{-5}$ s).

(k) Resonance fluorescence is a type of emission in which the radiation produced is identical in wavelength to that of the radiation that is used to excite the fluorescence.

(l) A *photon* is a bundle or a particle of radiant energy whose magnitude is given by $h\nu$, where h is the Planck constant and ν is the frequency of the radiation.

(m) *Absorptivity a* is defined by the equation

$$a = A/bc$$

where A is the absorbance of a medium contained in a cell length of b, where b may be expressed in cm or any other specified unit of length, and a concentration of c where c may be expressed in any specified concentration unit (such as g/L).

(n) The *wavenumber* of radiation is the reciprocal of the wavelength in centimeters.

(o) *Relaxation* is a process whereby an excited species loses energy and returns to a lower energy state.

(p) The *Stokes shift* is the difference in wavelength between the radiation used to excite fluorescence and the wavelength of the fluorescence itself.

6-2

$$\nu = \frac{c}{\lambda} = \frac{2.998 \times 10^{10} \text{ cm/s}}{2.70 \text{ Å} \times 10^{-8} \text{ cm/Å}} = \underline{\underline{1.11 \times 10^{18} \text{ Hz}}}$$

$$E = h\nu = 6.626 \times 10^{-34} \text{ Js} \times 1.11 \times 10^{18} \text{ s}^{-1} = \underline{\underline{7.36 \times 10^{-16} \text{ J}}}$$

$$E = 7.36 \times 10^{-16} \text{ J} \times 6.242 \times 10^{18} \text{ eV/ J} = \underline{\underline{4.59 \times 10^{3} \text{ eV}}}$$

6-3

$$\nu = \frac{c}{\lambda} = \frac{2.998 \times 10^{10} \text{ cm/s}}{5.715 \text{ }\mu\text{m} \times 10^{-4} \text{ cm/}\mu\text{m}} = \underline{\underline{5.246 \times 10^{13} \text{ s}^{-1}}}$$

$$\bar{\nu} = \frac{1}{\lambda} = \frac{1}{5.715 \times 10^{-4} \text{ cm}} = 1750 \text{ cm}^{-1}$$

$$E = h\nu = 6.626 \times 10^{-34} \text{ Js} \times 5.246 \times 10^{13} \text{ s}^{-1} = \underline{\underline{3.476 \times 10^{-20} \text{ J}}}$$

$$= 3.476 \times 10^{-20} \frac{\text{J}}{\text{photon}} \times 6.02 \times 10^{3} \frac{\text{photons}}{\text{mol}} \times 10^{-3} \frac{\text{kJ}}{\text{J}} = \underline{\underline{20.93 \frac{\text{kJ}}{\text{mol}}}}$$

6-4

$$\lambda = \frac{c}{\nu} = \frac{2.948 \times 10^{10} \text{ cm s}^{-1}}{220 \times 10^{6} \text{ s}^{-1}} = \underline{\underline{136 \text{ cm}}}$$

$$E = h\nu = 6.626 \times 10^{-34} \text{ Js} \times 220 \times 10^{6} \text{ s}^{-1} = \underline{\underline{1.46 \times 10^{-25} \text{ J}}}$$

6-5

$$\nu = \frac{c}{\lambda} = \frac{2.998 \times 10^{10} \text{ cm s}^{-1}}{589 \text{ nm} \times 10^{-7} \text{ cm nm}^{-1}} = \underline{\underline{5.09 \times 10^{14} \text{ s}^{-1}}}$$

$$v_{cell} = c/n_{D} = 2.998 \times 10^{10} \text{ cm s}^{-1} \times 1/1.43 = \underline{\underline{2.10 \times 10^{10} \text{ cm s}^{-1}}}$$

$$\lambda_{cell} = \frac{v_{cell}}{\nu} = \frac{2.10 \times 10^{10} \text{ cm s}^{-1}}{5.09 \times 10^{14} \text{ s}^{-1}} \times 10^{7} \frac{\text{nm}}{\text{cm}} = \underline{\underline{413 \text{ nm}}}$$

6-6

$$n_{D} = \frac{\sin 30}{\sin 11.9} = \underline{\underline{2.42}}$$

6-7

$$\nu = \frac{2.998 \times 10^{10} \text{ cm s}^{-1} \times 3}{500 \text{ nm} \times 10^{-7} \text{ cm/nm}} = \underline{\underline{1.80 \times 10^{15} \text{ s}^{-1}}}$$

$$\lambda = \frac{c}{\nu} = \frac{2.998 \times 10^{10} \text{ cm s}^{-1}}{1.80 \times 10^{15} \text{ s}^{-1}} \times \frac{10^{7} \text{ nm}}{\text{cm}} = \underline{\underline{167 \text{ nm}}}$$

6-8

$$E = 255 \frac{\text{kJ}}{\text{mol}} \times \frac{10^{3} \text{ J}}{\text{kJ}} \times \frac{1 \text{ mol}}{6.02 \times 10^{23} \text{ photons}} = 4.24 \times 10^{-19} \text{ J}$$

$$\nu = \frac{E}{h} = \frac{4.24 \times 10^{-19} \text{ J}}{6.626 \times 10^{-34} \text{ Js}} = 6.40 \times 10^{14} \text{ s}^{-1}$$

$$\lambda = \frac{c}{\nu} = \frac{2.998 \times 10^{10} \text{ cm s}^{-1}}{6.40 \times 10^{14} \text{ s}^{-1}} \times 10^{7} \frac{\text{nm}}{\text{cm}} = \underline{\underline{469 \text{ nm}}}$$

6-9 (a)

$$E_{660} = \frac{2.998 \times 10^{10} \text{ cm s}^{-1}}{660 \text{ nm} \times 10^{-7} \text{ cm/nm}} \times 6.626 \times 10^{-34} \text{ Js} = 3.01 \times 10^{-10} \text{ J}$$

$$E_{500} = \frac{2.98 \times 10^{10}}{500 \times 10^{-7}} \times 6.626 \times 10^{-34} = 3.973 \times 10^{-19} \text{ J}$$

$$E_{max} = 3.97 \times 10^{-19} - 3.01 \times 10^{-19} = \underline{9.63 \times 10^{-20}}$$

(b) The rest mass of the electron m is 9.11×10^{-31} kg . Then letting v be the velocity of the photoelectron in meters per second, we may write

$$E_{max} = 9.63 \times 10^{-20} \text{ J} = \frac{1}{2} mv^2 = \frac{1}{2} \times 9.11 \times 10^{-3} \text{ kg } v^2$$

and

$$v = \sqrt{\frac{2 \times 9.63 \times 10^{-20} \text{ kg m}^2 \cdot \text{s}^{-2}}{9.11 \times 10^{-31} \text{ kg}}} = \underline{4.60 \times 10^5 \text{ m/s}}$$

6-10 From Figure 6-18, λ_{max} at 3000 K is estimated to be 1100 nm.

$$k = T \cdot \lambda_{max} = 3000 \text{ K} \times 1100 \text{ nm} = \underline{3.3 \times 10^6 \text{ K} \cdot \text{nm}}$$

At 1400 K

$$\lambda_{max} = 3.3 \times 10^6 \text{ K} \cdot \text{nm}/1400 \text{ K} = 2.4 \times 10^3 \text{ nm} \quad \text{or} \quad \underline{2.4 \text{ } \mu\text{m}}$$

6-11 The wavelength in the aqueous solution is given by

$$\lambda_{aq} = v_{aq}/\nu \qquad \text{(Equation } 6-1)$$

where v_{aq} is the velocity. Letting n be the refractive index, we write

$$v_{aq} = c/n \qquad \text{(Equation } 6-11)$$

$$\nu = c/\lambda_{air} \qquad \text{(Equation } 6-2)$$

Substituting into the first equation yields after rearranging

$$\lambda_{aq} = \lambda_{air}/n$$

(a) $\lambda_{aq} = 589 \text{ nm}/1.35 = \underline{436 \text{ nm}}$

(b) $\lambda_{aq} = 694.3 \text{ nm}/1.55 = \underline{448 \text{ nm}}$

6-12 The fraction reflected in passing from air into quartz is

$$\frac{I_{R1}}{I_0} = \frac{(1.55 - 1.00)^2}{(1.55 + 1.00)^2} = 0.0465$$

Thus the intensity of the beam I_1 in the quartz is

$$I_1 = I_0 - 0.0465\,I_0 = 0.9535\,I_0$$

The intensity loss in passing from the quartz to air is

$$\frac{I_{R2}}{0.9535\,I_0} = 0.0465$$

$$I_{R2} = 0.443\,I_0$$

and the intensity in the interior of the cell I_2 is

$$I_2 = 0.9535\,I_0 - 0.0443\,I_0 = 0.9092\,I_0$$

The reflective loss in passing from the interior of the cell into the second quartz window

$$\frac{I_{R3}}{0.9092\,I_0} = 0.0465$$

$$I_{R3} = 0.0423\,I_0$$

and the intensity I_3 in the second quartz window

$$I_3 = 0.9092\,I_0 - 0.0423\,I_0 = 0.8669\,I_0$$

The intensity loss in passing from quartz to air is

$$\frac{I_{R4}}{0.8669\,I_0} = 0.0465$$

$$I_{R4} = 0.0403\,I_0$$

and the intensity of the beam I_4 upon again entering air

$$I_4 = 0.8669\,I_0 - 0.0403\,I_0 = 0.8266\,I_0$$

The total loss by reflection is

$$I_{RT} = 1 - 0.8226 = 0.173 \quad \text{or} \quad 17.3\%$$

6-13 The wave model of radiation requires that the radiation from a beam be evenly distributed over any surface it strikes. Under these circumstances, no single electron could gain sufficient energy rapidly enough to be ejected from the surface and thus provide an instantaneous current.

6-14 (a) T = antilog (- 0.375) = 0.422 or 42.2%. Similarly, (b) 4.73% (c) 97.3%

6-15 (a) $A = -\log(33.6/100) = \underline{0.474}$. Similarly, (b) $\underline{0.0357}$ (c) $\underline{1.76}$

6-16 (a) $T = $ antilog $(-0.375/2) = 0.649$ or $\underline{64.9\%}$. Similarly, (b) $\underline{21.8\%}$ (c) $98.6 \approx \underline{99\%}$

6-17 (a) $A = -\log(33.6/200) = \underline{0.775}$. Similarly, (b) $\underline{0.337}$ (c) $\underline{2.06}$

6-18 $A_1 = -\log 0.126 = 0.900 = \varepsilon b c_1 = \varepsilon \times 2.00 \times 4.14 \times 10^{-3}$

$A_2 = -\log(3 \times 0.126) = 0.423 = \varepsilon \times 1.00 \times c_2$

$$\frac{0.900}{0.423} = \frac{2 \times 4.14 \times 10^{-3}}{1.00 \times c_2}$$

$c_2 = 8.28 \times 10^{-3} \times 0.423/0.900 = \underline{3.89 \times 10^{-3} \text{ M}}$

6-19 $A = 2.17 \times 10^3 \times 2.50 \times c = -\log 0.0842$

$c = 1.07/(5.43 \times 10^3) = \underline{1.98 \times 10^{-4} \text{ M}}$

CHAPTER 7

7-1 Equation 7-15 can be written in the form $w = \Delta \lambda_{\text{eff}} / D^{-1}$. For a prism monochromator D^{-1}, the reciprocal linear dispersion, increases continuously as the wavelength becomes longer. Thus if $\Delta \lambda_{\text{eff}}$ is to retain constant, w, the slit width, must be decreased accordingly. For a grating instrument, D^{-1} is essentially constant over a considerable wavelength range. Thus w does not have to be varied.

7-2 For qualitative analysis, it is important to resolve the various peaks. This consideration often dictates the use of as narrow a slit width as possible. On the other hand, for quantitative work, wider slit widths usually result in better signal-to-noise ratios, which, in turn, lead to higher precision.

7-3 (a) $\lambda_{\text{max}} = 2.90 \times 10^3/4000 = \underline{0.725 \text{ μm}}$ or $\underline{725 \text{ nm}}$

(b) $\lambda_{\text{max}} = 2.90 \times 10^3/2000 = \underline{1.45 \text{ μm}}$

(c) $\lambda_{\text{max}} = 2.90 \times 10^3/1000 = \underline{2.90 \text{ μm}}$

7-4 (a) $E_T = 5.69 \times 10^{-8} \text{ W m}^{-2} \text{ K}^{-4} (4000 \text{ K})^4 = \underline{1.46 \times 10^7 \text{ W/m}^2}$

(b) $E_T = 5.69 \times 10^{-8} (2000)^4 = \underline{9.10 \times 10^5 \text{ W/m}^2}$

(c) $E_T = 5.69 \times 10^{-8} (1000)^4 = \underline{5.69 \times 10^4 \text{ W/m}^2}$

7-5 (a) $\lambda_{max} = 2.90 \times 10^3/2870 = \underline{\underline{1.01 \, \mu m \quad \text{or} \quad 1010 \, nm}}$

$\lambda_{max} = 2.90 \times 10^3/3000 = \underline{\underline{0.967 \, \mu m \quad \text{or} \quad 967 \, nm}}$

(b) $E_T = 5.69 \times 10^{-8} (2870)^4 = \underline{\underline{3.86 \times 10^6 W/m^2}}$

$E_T = 5.69 \times 10^{-8} (3000)^4 = \underline{\underline{4.61 \times 10^6 \, W/m^2}}$

7-6 Spontaneous emission occurs when a species loses all or part of its excess energy in the form of fluorescent radiation. Because the process is random and can occur in any direction, the radiation is incoherent.

Stimulated emission is brought about by interaction of excited particles with externally produced photons that have energies that exactly match the energy difference between the excited state and some lower energy level. The photons produced are in phase with those triggering the stimulated emission; coherent radiation is the result.

7-7 A four-level laser system has the advantage that population inversion is achieved with less pumping than is required for a three-level system. In a four-level system it is only necessary to maintain a number of excited species that exceeds the number in an intermediate energy level that is higher in energy than the ground state. If the lifetime of the intermediate state is brief, a relatively few excited species is required for population inversion.

7-8 The effective bandwidth of a filter is the width in wavelength units of the band transmitted by the filter when measured at one half the peak height.

7-9 (a) $\lambda = 4.54 = \dfrac{2 tn}{n}$ (Equation 7 – 5)

$t = \lambda n/2n = 4.54 \times 1/(2 \times 1.34) = \underline{\underline{1.69 \, \mu m}}$

(b) For second-order, $\lambda_2 = 2 \times 1.69 \times 1.34/2 = \underline{\underline{2.27 \, \mu m}}$

For third-order, $\lambda_3 = 2 \times 1.69 \times 1.34/3 = \underline{\underline{1.51 \, \mu m, \text{etc.}}}$

7-10 From Equation 7-5, $t = \lambda n/2n$

If first-order interference is used, one end of the wedge would have a thickness t of

$t = 700 \times 1/(2 \times 1.32) = 265 \, nm \quad \text{or} \quad 0.265 \, \mu m$

This thickness would also transmit second-order radiation of $700/2 = 350 \, nm$, which would be absorbed by the glass plates supporting the wedge.

The other end of the wedge should have thickness of

$t = 400 \times 1/(2 \times 1.32) = 1.52 \, nm \quad \text{or} \quad 0.152 \, \mu m$

Thus, a layer should be deposited which is 0.265 μm on one end and which tapers linearly over 10 cm to 0.152 μm.

7-11 The dispersion of glass for visible radiation is considerably greater than that for fused silica or quartz (see Figure 6-9).

7-12 $n\lambda = d(\sin i + \sin r)$ (Equation 7 − 6)

$d = n\lambda/(\sin i + \sin r) = 1 \times 500/(\sin 60 + \sin 10)$

$= 500/(0.8660 + 0.1736) = 480.9$ nm

$$\text{lines/mm} = \frac{1 \text{ line}}{480.9 \text{ nm}} \times 10^6 \frac{\text{nm}}{\text{mm}} = \underline{\underline{2079}}$$

7-13 For first-order diffraction, Equation 7-13 takes the form

$$\lambda/\Delta\lambda = nN = 1 \times 10.0 \text{ mm} \times 72.0 \text{ lines/mm} = \underline{\underline{720 \text{ lines}}}$$

In order to obtain the resolution in units of cm^{-1}, we differentiate the equation $\lambda = 1/\overline{\nu}$

$$\frac{d\lambda}{d\overline{\nu}} = -\frac{1}{\overline{\nu}^2} \quad \text{or} \quad \frac{\Delta\lambda}{\Delta\overline{\nu}} = -\frac{1}{\overline{\nu}^2}$$

Thus

$$\Delta\lambda = -\Delta\overline{\nu}/(\overline{\nu})^2$$

Substituting for λ and $\Delta\lambda$ into the first equation give

$$-\frac{1/\overline{\nu}}{\Delta\overline{\nu}/(\overline{\nu})^2} = -\frac{\overline{\nu}}{\Delta\overline{\nu}} = 720$$

$$\Delta\overline{\nu} = -\frac{\overline{\nu}}{720} = -\frac{10^3 \text{ cm}^{-1}}{720} = \underline{\underline{-1.39 \text{ cm}^{-1}}}$$

Here the minus sign has no significance.

7-14 $n\lambda = d(\sin i + \sin r)$ (Equation 7 − 6)

where $d = 1$ mm/72 lines $= 0.01389$ mm/line or 13.9 μm/line

For n = 1

(a) $\lambda = 13.9 [\sin 50 + \sin(+20)] = \underline{\underline{15.4 \text{ μm}}}$

and for n = 2, $\lambda = \underline{\underline{7.7 \text{ μm}}}$

Similarly,

(b) <u>10.6   and   5.3 μm</u>

7-15

	Source	Wavelength Selector	Sample Holder	Photomultiplier	Readout
(a)	W lamp	Glass prism	Glass window	Photomultiplier tube	Chart
(b)	Globar	Grating, ~50 lines/m	KBr window	Golay cell	Chart
(c)	W lamp	Green filter	Pyrex test tube	Barrier cell	Meter
(d)	Nichrome wire	Interference filter	TlBr/TlI window	Thermocouple	Meter
(e)	Gas/oxygen flame	Quartz prism	Flame	Photomultiplier tube	Chart
(f)	Argon lamp	Grating, ~3000 lines/m	KBr window	Photomultiplier	Chart
(g)	W lamp	Glass or quartz prism	Glass window	Photoconductor	Chart

7-16 $f = F/d$ (Equation 7 − 14)

$\quad = 8.2/4.2 = \underline{1.95}$

7-17 $f = 8.2/4.2 = 3.1$

$$\frac{\text{light gathering power of } f \text{ 1.9 lens}}{\text{light gathering power of } f \text{ 3.1 lens}} = \frac{(3.1)^2}{(1.95)^2} = \underline{\underline{2.5}}$$

7-18 (a)

$$R = n\mathrm{V} = 1 \times 1250 \frac{\text{lines}}{\text{mm}} \times \frac{10\ \text{mm}}{\text{cm}} \times 2.00\ \text{cm} = \underline{\underline{2.50 \times 10^4}} \quad \text{(Equation 7 − 13)}$$

(b)

$$D_1^{-1} = \frac{d}{nF} = \frac{(1\ \text{mm}/1250\ \text{lines}) \times 10^6\ \text{nm/mm}}{1 \times 1.6\ \text{m} \times 10^3\ \text{mm/m}} \quad \text{(Equation 7 − 11)}$$

$$= \underline{\underline{0.50\ \text{nm/mm}}}$$

$$D_2^{-1} = 0.50/2 = \underline{\underline{0.25\ \text{nm/mm}}}$$

31

7-19 (a) $D^{-1} = \dfrac{(1\ m/2000\ lines) \times 10^6\ nm/m}{1 \times 0.65\ m \times 10^3\ mm/m} = \underline{\underline{0.77\ nm/mm}}$ (see Solution 7 − 18)

(b) $R = nN = 1 \times 2000\ (lines/mm) \times 3.0\ mm = \underline{\underline{6.0 \times 10^3}}$

(c) $\lambda/\Delta\lambda = R = 6.0 \times 10^3 = \underline{\underline{560/\Delta\lambda}}$

$\Delta\lambda = 560/6.0 \times 10^3 = \underline{\underline{0.093\ nm}}$

7-20 A silicon diode detector is a *pn* junction operated under reverse bias. Photons striking the depletion layer create electrons and holes giving a current that is proportional to the number of photons.

7-21 (a) A spectroscope is an optical instrument for the visual identification of emission lines. It consists of a monochromator in which the exit slit is replaced by an eyepiece that can be moved along the focal phase. The wavelength of an emission line is determined from the angle between the incident beam and the dispersed beam when the line is centered on the eyepiece.

(b) A spectrograph is a monochromator with a large aperture that allows a wide range of wavelengths to strike a detector located on the focal plane simultaneously. The detector in this type of instrument is either a photographic plate or multichannel transducer such as a linear photodiode (see Section 7E-3).

(c) A spectrophotometer is a monochromator with a photodetector located at its exit slit. Provision is made for moving the dispersing element so various portions of the spectrum can be focused on the slit.

7-22 $f = 2v_M/\lambda$ (Equation 7 − 23)

(a) $f = \dfrac{2 \times 1.25\ cm/s}{300\ nm/cycle \times 10^{-7}\ cm/nm} = 8.33 \times 10^4\ cycle/s = \underline{\underline{8.33 \times 10^4\ Hz}}$

(b) $f = 2.50/(700 \times 10^{-7}) = \underline{\underline{3.57 \times 10^4\ Hz}}$

(c) $f = 2.50/(7.5 \times 10^{-4}) = \underline{\underline{3.33 \times 10^3\ Hz}}$

(d) $f = 2.50/20 \times 10^{-4}) = \underline{\underline{1.25 \times 10^3\ Hz}}$

7-23 (a) $\overline{v}_2 - \overline{v}_1 = \dfrac{1}{\delta}$ (Equation 7 − 33)

At 20.34 μm, $\overline{v}_2 = 4.9164 \times 10^2\ cm^{-1}$

At 20.35 μm, $\overline{v}_1 = 4.9140 \times 10^2\ cm^{-1}$

$\overline{v}_2 - \overline{v}_1 = 0.24\ cm^{-1}$ and $\delta = 1/0.24 = 4.2\ cm$

length of drive $= 4.2/2 = \underline{\underline{2.1 \text{ cm}}}$

(b) In the same way,

at 2.500 µm, $4.0000 \times 10^3 \text{ cm}^{-1}$

at 2.501 µm, $3.9984 \times 10^3 \text{ cm}^{-1}$

$\bar{v}_2 - \bar{v}_1 = 1.59 \text{ cm}^{-1}$ and $\delta = 1/1.59 = 0.629 \text{ cm}$

length of drive $= 0.629/2 = \underline{\underline{0.314 \text{ cm}}}$

CHAPTER 8

8-1 The flame absorption peak for calcium in a low-temperature flame is broad because the calcium is largely present as the calcium molecule CaOH, which has many vibrational and rotational states and thus many excited energy levels. Thus a broad molecular absorption peak is observed. In contrast, barium is apparently present only as atoms that only absorb at a few discrete wavelengths.

8-2 Resonance fluorescence is a type of fluorescence in which the emitted radiation has a wavelength that is identical to the wavelength of the radiation used to excite the fluorescence.

8-3 Fluorescence will occur at a longer wavelength (the Stokes shift) than the excitation wavelength when relaxation takes place by combination of fluorescence and vibrational relaxation.

8-4 Natural line widths in atomic spectroscopy are the widths of lines when only the uncertainty principle, and not Doppler and pressure broadening, contribute to the broadening.

8-5 In the presence of KCl ionization of sodium is avoided because of the high concentration of electrons from ionization of potassium. In the absence of KCl some of the sodium is ionized, which leads to a lower intensity of the emission line for atomic sodium.

8-6 The energy necessary to promote a ground state s electron to the next p level is so high for Cs that only a fraction of Cs atoms are excited at the temperature of a natural gas flame. At the higher temperature of a hydrogen/oxygen flame a much larger fraction of the atoms is excited and thus emit a more intense Cs line.

8-7 A continuous type of atomizer is a flame. A noncontinuous type of atomizer is an electrothermal furnace. The former provides an output that is essentially constant with time. The latter produces a signal that arises to a maximum with time and then decreases to zero.

8-8 (a) $v = \sqrt{8kT/\pi m}$

From the table of energy conversion factors (inside the front cover of the text), the Boltzmann constant k is equal to

$$k \;=\; 1.38 \times 10^{-23} \text{ kg m}^2\text{s}^{-2}\,\text{K}^{-1}$$

Thus

$$v \;=\; \sqrt{\dfrac{8 \times 1.38 \times 10^{-23}\ \text{kg m}^2\,\text{s}^{-2}\,\text{K}^{-1} \times 2200\ \text{K}}{\pi \times 23.0 \times 10^{-3}(\text{kg Na/mol})/(6.02 \times 10^{23}\ \text{particles Na/mol})}}$$

$$=\; 1.42 \times 10^{3}\ \text{m/s}$$

$$\Delta\lambda \;=\; \dfrac{v\lambda}{c} \;=\; \dfrac{1.42 \times 10^{3}\ \text{m} \cdot \text{s}^{-1} \times 5893\ \text{Å} \times 10^{-10}\ \text{m/Å}}{3.00 \times 10^{8}\ \text{m} \cdot \text{s}^{-1}}$$

$$=\; 2.79 \times 10^{-12}\ \text{m} \quad \text{or} \quad \underline{\underline{0.028\ \text{Å}}}$$

(b) Proceeding in the same way, we find at 3000 K, $\Delta\lambda \;=\; \underline{\underline{0.033\ \text{Å}}}$

8-9 The energies of the $3p$ states can be obtained from the emission wavelengths shown in Figure 8-1. For sodium we will use an average wavelength of 5893 Å and for Mg⁺, 2800 Å.

For Na, the energy of the excited state is

$$E_{y1} \;=\; \dfrac{hc}{\lambda} \;=\; \dfrac{6.62 \times 10^{-34}\ \text{Js} \times 3.00 \times 10^{8}\ \text{m} \cdot \text{s}^{-1}}{5893\ \text{Å} \times 10^{-10}\ \text{m/Å}} \;=\; 3.37 \times 10^{-19}\ \text{J}$$

For Mg⁺

$$E_{y2} \;-\; \dfrac{6.62 \times 10^{-34} \times 3.00 \times 10^{8}}{2800 \times 10^{-10}} \;=\; 7.09 \times 10^{-19}\ \text{J}$$

(a) Substituting into Equation 8-1 (page 199) gives for 2100 K,

$$N_{j1}/N_0 \;=\; 3\exp\left(-\dfrac{3.37 \times 10^{-19}\ \text{J}}{1.38 \times 10^{-23}\ \text{JK}^{-1} \times 2100\ \text{K}}\right) \;=\; \underline{\underline{2.7 \times 10^{-5}}}$$

$$N_{j2}/N_0 \;=\; 3\exp\left(-\dfrac{7.09 \times 10^{-19}}{1.38 \times 10^{23} \times 2100}\right) \;=\; \underline{\underline{7.1 \times 10^{-11}}}$$

Proceeding in the same way, we obtain for Na and Mg⁺ respectively,

(b) $N_j/N_0 \;=\; 6.6 \times 10^{-4}$ and 6.1×10^{-8}

(c) $N_j/N_0 \;=\; 5.1 \times 10^{-2}$ and 5.7×10^{-4}

8-10 The energy difference between the $3p$ and $3s$ state for sodium was shown in Solution 8-9 to be $E_y \;=\; 3.37 \times 10^{-19}\ \text{J}$. The energy difference between the $4s$ and $3p$ state E_y' can be calculated from the wavelength of the emission lines at 1139 nm.

$$E_y' = \frac{6.62 \times 10^{-34}\ J\,s \times 3.00 \times 10^8\ m\,s^{-1}}{1139\ nm \times 10^{-9}\ nm/mm} = 1.74 \times 10^{-19}\ J$$

The energy difference between the 4s and 3s state is

$$E_y'' = 3.37 \times 10^{-19} + 1.74 \times 10^{-19} = 5.11 \times 10^{-19}\ J$$

Applying Equation 8-1 gives

(a) At $3000°C = 3273\ K$

$$\frac{N_{4s}}{N_{3s}} = \frac{2}{2}\exp\left(-\frac{5.11 \times 10^{-19}\ J}{1.38 \times 10^{-23}\ J\,K^{-1} \times 3272}\right) = \underline{\underline{1.2 \times 10^{-5}}}$$

(b) At $9000°C = 9273\ K$

$$\frac{N_{4s}}{N_{3s}} = \exp\left(-\frac{5.11 \times 10^{-19}}{1.38 \times 10^{-23} \times 9273}\right) = \underline{\underline{1.8 \times 10^{-2}}}$$

8-11 This behavior would result from ionization of the U. At low concentrations, the fraction of U that is ionized would be greater thus giving a nonlinear relationship between concentration and absorbance.

CHAPTER 9

9-1 (a) A *releasing agent* is a cation which preferentially reacts with a species that would otherwise react with the analyte to cause a chemical interference.

(b) *Protective agents* prevent interference by forming stable and volatile products with the analyte.

(c) An *ionization suppressor* provides a high concentration of electrons in the flame. These electrons suppress ionization of the analyte.

(d) *Atomization* is the process in which a sample is vaporized and decomposed to its atoms, usually by heat.

(e) *Pressure broadening* refers to the broadening of atomic line widths at higher concentrations of atoms in a flame.

(f) A *hollow cathode lamp* (Figure 9-11) has a tungsten anode and a cylindric-shaped cathode containing the element of interest. The element is sputtered from the cathode into the gas phase. This process excites some of the gaseous atoms, which then emit their characteristic radiation as they return to the ground state.

(g) *Sputtering* is the process in which gaseous cations bombard a cathode and eject atoms from the cathode into the gas phase.

(h) *Self-absorption* refers to the absorption of radiation by unexcited atoms in the gas phase of a hollow cathode lamp or other source.

(i) *Spectral interference* is encountered when the absorption or emission of a nonanalyte species overlaps a peak being used for the determination of the analyte.

(j) *Chemical interference* is the result of any chemical process which decreases or increases the absorption or emission characteristics of the analyte.

(k) A *radiation buffer* is a substance added in excess to both sample and standards, which swamps out the effect of the sample matrix on the analyte emission or absorption.

(l) *Doppler broadening* arises because atoms moving toward or away from the monochromator give rise to absorption or emission lines at slightly different frequencies.

9-2 The absorbance of Cr decreases with increasing flame height because chromium oxides are formed to a greater and greater extent as the Cr rises through the flame. The Ag absorbance increases as the silver becomes more atomized as it rises through the flame. Silver oxides are not readily formed. Magnesium exhibits a maximum as a result of both effects mentioned above opposing each other.

9-3 The electrothermal atomizer requires less sample and keeps the sample in the optical beam for a much longer time than does a flame.

9-4 The continuous radiation from the deuterium lamp is passed through the flame alternately with the hollow cathode lamp beam. By comparing the power of the beams, it is possible to continuously correct the signal power for the variable attenuation encountered during sample aspiration in the flame.

9-5 Source modulation is employed to distinguish between the component of light arising from the source and the component of light arising from the flame background.

9-6 The alcohol reduces the surface tension of the solution thus leading to smaller droplets, a greater number of which then reach the flame in a given unit of time. Thus, a greater number of Ni atoms are present at any instant.

9-7 At high currents, more unexcited atoms are formed in the sputtering process. These atoms generally have less kinetic energy than the excited ones. The Doppler broadening of their absorption lines is therefore less than the broadening of the emission lines of the faster moving excited atoms. Thus, only the center of the emission line is attenuated by self-absorption.

9-8 (1) Employ a higher temperature flame (acetylene/oxygen). (2) Employ a solvent that contains ethanol or other organic substances. (3) Add a releasing agent or a protective agent.

9-9 The population of excited molecules, from which emission arises, is very sensitive to the flame temperature. The population of ground state molecules, from which absorption and fluorescence originate, is not very sensitive to temperature.

9-10 (a) Nebulization. Mg^{2+} and Cl^- in water are converted to aqueous aerosol.

(b) Desolvation. Mg^{2+} and Cl^- in aqueous aerosol converted to $MgCl_2$ plus water (liquid and vapor).

(c) Volatilization. Remaining water stripped away leaving $MgCl_2$.

(d) Atomization. Produces Mg^0 atoms.

(e) Excitation of Mg^0 to Mg^*.

(f) Ionization of Mg^0 to Mg^{1+}.

(g) Reaction of Mg^0 to MgOH or MgO.

9-11
$$R = \frac{\lambda}{\Delta\lambda} = nN = \frac{500\,\text{nm}}{0.002\,\text{nm}} = 2.5 \times 10^5 = 1 \times N$$

$$N = \text{no. of blazes} = 2.5 \times 10^5$$

$$\text{Size of grating} = \frac{2.5 \times 10^5\,\text{grooves}}{2400\,\text{grooves/mm}} = \underline{\underline{104\,\text{mm}}}$$

9-12 The flame temperature at the four heights are estimated to be 1700, 1863, 1820, and 1725°C or 1973, 2136, 2092, and 1998 K. In order to obtain E_j in Equation 8-1 (page 199), we employ Equation 6-19 (page 130). Then

$$E_j = \frac{hc}{\lambda} = \frac{6.62 \times 10^{-34}\,\text{J s} \times 3.00 \times 10^8\,\text{m} \cdot \text{s}^{-1}}{766.5 \times 10^{-9}\,\text{m}} = 2.59 \times 10^{-19}\,\text{J}$$

Substituting into Equation (8-1) gives

$$\frac{N_j}{N_0} = 3\exp\left(-\frac{2.59 \times 10^{-19}\,\text{J}}{1.38 \times 10^{-23}\,\text{J K}^{-1} \times 1973\,\text{K}}\right) = \underline{\underline{2.22 \times 10^{-4}}}$$

Proceeding in the same way, we find

Height	T	$(N_j/N_0) \times 10^4$	$I_{(x\,cm)}/I_{(y\,cm)}$
(a) 2.0	1973	2.22	1.00
(b) 3.0	2136	4.58	2.07
(c) 4.0	2092	3.81	1.72
(d) 5.0	1998	2.50	1.13

9-13 (a) Sulfate ion forms complexes with Fe(III) that are not readily atomized. Thus the concentration of iron atoms in a flame is less in the presence of sulfate ions.

(b) Sulfate interference could be overcome by (1) adding a releasing agent that forms complexes with sulfate that are more stable than the iron complexes, (2) adding a protective agent, such as EDTA, that forms a highly stable but volatile complexes with the Fe(III), and (3) by employing a higher temperature flame (oxygen/acetylene or nitrous oxide/acetylene).

9-14 The energies of the 3p states can be obtained from the emission wavelengths shown in Figure 8-1. For sodium we will use an average wavelength of 5893 Å and for Mg⁺, 2800 Å.

For Na, the energy of the excited state is

$$E_{y1} \;=\; \frac{hc}{\lambda} \;=\; \frac{6.62 \times 10^{-34}\ \text{Js} \times 3.00 \times 10^{8}\ \text{m} \cdot \text{s}^{-1}}{5893\ \text{Å} \times 10^{-10}\ \text{m/Å}} \;=\; 3.37 \times 10^{-19}\ \text{J}$$

For Mg

$$E_{y2} \;=\; \frac{6.62 \times 10^{-34} \times 3.00 \times 10^{8}}{2800 \times 10^{-10}} \;=\; 7.09 \times 10^{-19}\ \text{J}$$

(a) Substituting into Equation 8-1 (page 199) gives for 2100 K,

$$N_{j1}/N_0 \;=\; 3\exp\!\left(-\frac{3.37 \times 10^{-19}\ \text{J}}{1.38 \times 10^{-23}\ \text{J K}^{-1} \times 2100\ \text{K}}\right) \;=\; \underline{\underline{2.7 \times 10^{-5}}}$$

$$N_{j2}/N_0 \;=\; 3\exp\!\left(-\frac{7.09 \times 10^{-19}}{1.38 \times 10^{-23} \times 2100}\right) \;=\; \underline{\underline{7.1 \times 10^{-11}}}$$

Proceeding in the same way, we obtain for Na and Mg⁺ respectively, $N_j/N_0 =$

(b) 6.6×10^{-4} and 6.1×10^{-8}

(c) 5.1×10^{-2} and 5.7×10^{-4}

9-15 The energy difference between the 3p and 3s state for sodium was shown in Solution 9-14 to be $E_y = 3.37 \times 10^{-19}$ J. The energy difference between the 4s and 3p state E_y' can be calculated from the wavelength of the emission lines at 1139 nm.

$$E_y' \;=\; \frac{6.62 \times 10^{-34}\ \text{Js} \times 3.00 \times 10^{8}\ \text{m s}^{-1}}{1139\ \text{nm} \times 10^{-9}\ \text{nm/mm}} \;=\; 1.74 \times 10^{-19}\ \text{J}$$

The energy difference between the 4s and 3s state is

$$E_y'' \;=\; 3.37 \times 10^{-19} + 1.74 \times 10^{-19} \;=\; 5.11 \times 10^{-19}\ \text{J}$$

(a) At 3000°C ≡ 3272 K

Applying Equation 8-1, gives

$$\frac{N_{4s}}{N_{3s}} \;=\; \frac{2}{2}\exp\!\left(-\frac{5.11 \times 10^{-19}\ \text{J}}{1.35 \times 10^{-23}\ \text{J K}^{-1} \times 3272}\right) \;=\; \underline{\underline{1.2 \times 10^{-5}}}$$

(b) At 9000°C = 9273 K

$$\frac{N_{4s}}{N_{3s}} = \exp\left(-\frac{5.11 \times 10^{-19} \text{ J}}{1.38 \times 10^{-23} \times 9273}\right) = \underline{\underline{1.8 \times 10^{-2}}}$$

9-16 The absorbance of the three standards is estimated to be 0.32, 0.18, and 0.090. The absorbance of the unknown was taken as 0.17. From a least-squares treatment of the data the concentration is 0.099 (± 0.0080 μg Pb/mL.

9-17 During drying and ashing volatile absorbing species may have been formed. In addition, particulate matter would appear as smoke during ashing, which would scatter the source radiation thus reducing its intensity.

9-18 This behavior would result from ionization of the U. At low concentrations, the fraction of U that is ionized would be greater thus giving a nonlinear relationship between concentration and absorbance.

9-19 When an internal standard is used, the ratio of intensity of the analyte line to that of the internal standard is plotted as a function of concentration of the analyte. If the internal standard and the analyte species are influenced in the same way by variation in the aspiration rate and temperature of the source and if the internal standard is present at the same concentration in the calibration standards and unknown, this concentration ratio should be independent of these variables.

9-20 By linear interpolation, we obtain

$$c = 0.250 + (0.450 - 0.250)\left(\frac{0.444 - 0.396}{0.599 - 0.396}\right) = \underline{\underline{0.297 \text{ ppm Pb}}}$$

9-21 (a) A plot of the data reveals a linear relationship between the instrument reading y and μg Na_2O/mL.

(b) Proceeding as in Example a1-12 (Appendix 1), we obtain

$$\sum x_i = 200.0 \quad \text{and} \quad \sum x_i^2 = 12000$$

$$\sum y_i = 199.9 \quad \text{and} \quad \sum y_i^2 = 11380.37$$

$$\sum x_i y_i = 11676.00$$

Substituting into Equations a1-29, a1-30, and a1-31 gives

$$S_{xx} = \sum x_i^2 - (\sum x_i)^2/N = 12000 - (200.0)^2/5 = 4000.00$$

$$S_{yy} = \sum y_i^2 - (\sum y_i)^2/N = 11380.37 - (199.9)^2/5 = 3388.368$$

$$S_{xy} = \sum x_i y_i - \sum x_i \sum y_i/N = 11676.00 - (200.0 \times 199.9)/5 = 3680.00$$

$$m = \frac{3680.00}{4000.00} = 0.9200$$

$$b = \sum y_i/N - 0.9200 \sum x_i/N = 199.90/5 - 0.9200 \times 200.0/5 = 3.180$$

$$\underline{y \; = \; b + mx \; = \; 3.18 + 0.920\,x}$$

where y = photometric reading and x = $\mu g\ Na_2O/mL$.

(c) $\quad s_y \;=\; \sqrt{\dfrac{S_{yy} - m^2 S_{xx}}{N-2}} \;=\; \sqrt{\dfrac{3388.368 - (0.920)^2 \times 4000}{5-2}} \;=\; 0.961 \;=\; \underline{0.96}$

$\quad s_m \;=\; s_y/\sqrt{S_{xx}} \;=\; 0.961/\sqrt{4000} \;=\; 0.0152 \;=\; \underline{0.015}$

$\quad s_b \;=\; s_y \sqrt{\dfrac{1}{N - (\sum x_i)^2/\sum x_i^2}} \;=\; 0.961 \sqrt{\dfrac{1}{5 - (200.0)^2/12000}}$

$\qquad\quad = \; 0.744 \;=\; \underline{0.74}$

(d) $\quad \overline{x}_c \;=\; (\overline{y}_c - b)/m \;=\; (\overline{y}_c - 3.18)/0.920$

$\quad$ For blank, $\quad \overline{y}_c \;=\; (5.1 + 4.8 + 4.9)/3 \;=\; 4.933$

$\qquad\qquad\quad \overline{x}_c \;=\; (4.933 - 3.18)/0.920 \;=\; 1.91\ \mu g/mL$

$\qquad\qquad\quad s_c \;=\; \dfrac{s_y}{m} \sqrt{\dfrac{1}{L} + \dfrac{1}{N} + \dfrac{(\overline{y}_c - \overline{y})^2}{m^2 S_{xx}}}$

$\qquad\qquad\qquad = \; \dfrac{0.961}{0.92} \sqrt{\dfrac{1}{3} + \dfrac{1}{5} + \dfrac{(4.93 - 199.9/5)^2}{(0.920)^2 4000}}$

$\qquad\qquad\qquad = \; 0.99\ \mu g\ Na_2O/mL$

$\quad$ For sample A, $\quad \overline{y}_c \;=\; (28.6 + 28.2 + 28.9)/3 \;=\; 28.567$

$\qquad\qquad\qquad \overline{x}_c \;=\; (28.567 - 3.18)/0.920 \;=\; 27.59\ \mu g\ Na_2O/mL$

$\qquad\qquad\qquad s_c \;=\; \dfrac{0.61}{0.92} \sqrt{\dfrac{1}{3} + \dfrac{1}{5} + \dfrac{(28.57 - 199.9/5)^2}{(0.920)^2 4000}}$

$\qquad\qquad\qquad = \; 0.79\ \mu g\ Na_2O/mL$

$\mu g/mL\ Na_2O$ in sample = $27.59 - 1.91 = 25.7$

The absolute standard deviation for the difference s_d is given by

$$s_d \;=\; \sqrt{(0.99)^2 + (0.79)^2} \;=\; 1.27\ \mu g\ Na_2O/mL$$

$$\%\,Na_2O \;=\; \dfrac{(25.7\ \mu g\ Na_2O/mL)}{1.00\ g\ sample \times 10^6\ \mu g/g} \times 100\% \;=\; 0.257\%$$

The relative standard deviation of this result is determined by the relative standard deviation of 25.7 µg Na_2O/mL. Then

$$(s)_y = \frac{1.27}{25.7} \times 1000 = \underline{49\ ppt}$$

and the absolute standard deviation is given by

$$s = (49/1000) \times 0.257 = \underline{0.013\ \%\ Na_2O}$$

or $\%Na_2O = \underline{0.26 \pm 0.01}$

The data for samples B and C were treated in the same way giving:

	Blank	A	B	C
Ave meter reading, $\bar{x}_i$	4.933	28.567	40.700	72.600
Ave concn Na_2O, µg/mL, $\bar{y}_c$	1.91	27.59	40.78	75.46
Std dev, µg Na_2O/mL	0.99	0.79	0.76	1.05
Concn Na_2O corrected				
for blank	0.00	25.68	38.87	73.55
% Na_2O		0.257	0.389	0.736
Rel std dev, %		4.9	3.2	2.0
Abs std dev, % Na_2O		0.013	0.012	0.015

9-22 (a) A plot of the data reveals a straight line relationship between absorbance and milliliter of standard.

(b) Proceeding as in Example a1-12 (Appendix 1), we obtain

$$S_{xx} = \Sigma x_i^2 - (\Sigma x_i)^2/N = 3000.00 - (100)^2/5 = 1000.00$$

$$S_{yy} = \Sigma y_i^2 - (\Sigma y_i)^2/N = 0.793554 - (1.892)^2/5 = 0.0776212$$

$$S_{xy} = \Sigma x_i y_i - \Sigma x_i \Sigma y_i/N = 46.65 - 100 \times 1.892/5 = 8.810$$

$$m = S_{xy}/S_{xx} = 8.810/1000 = \underline{8.81 \times 10^{-3}}$$

$$b = \bar{y} - m\bar{x} = 1.892/5 - (8.81 \times 10^{-3}) \times 100/5 = \underline{0.202}$$

$$A = \underline{0.202 + 8.81 \times 10^{-3} \times mL\ std}$$

(c)
$$s_y = \sqrt{\frac{S_{yy} - m^2 S_{xy}}{N - 2}}$$

$$= \sqrt{\frac{0.0776212 - (8.81 \times 10^{-3})^2 \times 1000}{5 - 2}} = 1.30 \times 10^{-3} = \underline{\underline{1.3 \times 10^{-3}}}$$

$$s_m = \sqrt{\frac{(1.30 \times 10^{-3})^2}{1000}} = 4.12 \times 10^{-5} = \underline{\underline{4.1 \times 10^{-5}}}$$

$$s_b = s_y \sqrt{\frac{1}{N - (\sum x_i)^2 / \sum x_i^2}}$$

$$= 1.30 \times 10^{-3} \sqrt{\frac{1}{5 - (100)^2/3000}} = 1.01 \times 10^{-3} = \underline{\underline{1.0 \times 10^{-3}}}$$

(d) Employing Equation 1-11 (page 16)

$$c_x = \frac{b c_s}{m V_x} = \frac{0.202}{8.81 \times 10^{-3}} \times \frac{12.2}{10.0} = \underline{\underline{28.0 \text{ ppm Cr}}}$$

(e) Employing Equation 1-12 (page 17)

$$s_c = c_x \sqrt{\left(\frac{s_y}{b}\right)^2 + \left(\frac{s_m}{m}\right)^2}$$

$$= 28.0 \sqrt{\left(\frac{1.30 \times 10^{-3}}{0.202}\right)^2 + \left(\frac{4.12 \times 10^{-5}}{8.81 \times 10^{-3}}\right)^2} = \underline{\underline{0.22 \text{ ppm}}}$$

CHAPTER 10

10-1 An internal standard is a substance that responds to uncontrollable variables in a similar way as the analyte. It is introduced into, or is present in, both standards and samples in a fixed amount. The ratio of the analyte signal to the internal standard then serves as the analytical signal.

10-2 Flame atomic absorption methods require a separate lamp for each element, which is not convenient when several elements are to be determined.

10-3 The temperature of a spark plasma is so great (~ 40,000 K) that most atoms present are ionized. In a lower temperature arc (~ 4000 K) only the lighter elements are ionized to any significant extent. In a plasma, the high concentration of electrons prevents extensive ionization of the analyte atoms.

10-4 $D^{-1} = (2d \cos \beta)/nF$ Equation 7 − 16 (page 163)

(a)

$$D^{-1} = \frac{2 \times \frac{1\,mm}{100\,grooves} \times \frac{10^7\,\text{Å}}{mm} \times \cos 63°20'}{30 \times 0.75\ m \times 10^3\ mm/m} = \underline{\underline{4.0\ \text{Å}/mm}}$$

(b)

$$D^{-1} = \frac{2 \times \frac{1\,mm}{100\,grooves} \times \frac{10^7\,\text{Å}}{mm} \times \cos 63°20'}{100 \times 0.75\ m \times 10^3\ mm/m} = \underline{\underline{1.20\ \text{Å}/mm}}$$

10-5 In the presence of air and with graphite electrodes, strong cyanogen (CN) bands render the wavelength region of 350 to 420 nm of little use for analyses. By excluding nitrogen with an inert gas, the intensities of these bonds are greatly reduced making possible detection of several elements with lines in this region.

10-6 By nebulization, by electrothermal vaporization, and by a high-voltage electric spark.

10-7 The advantages of the ICP torch over dc argon plasma sources are higher sensitivity for several elements and freedom from maintenance problems. Advantages of dc plasma sources include lower argon consumption and simpler and less expensive equipment. A disadvantage of dc plasma sources is that their graphite electrodes must be replaced every few hours.

10-8 Ionization interferences are less severe in ICP than in flame emission spectroscopy because argon plasmas contain a high concentration of electrons (from ionization of the argon) that repress ionization of analyte atoms.

10-9 Advantages of plasma sources over flame sources include:

(1) Lower interelement interference.

(2) Emission spectra for most elements can be obtained with a single set of excitation conditions.

(3) Spectra can be obtained for low concentrations of elements that tend to form refractory compounds.

(4) Plasma sources usually have concentration ranges that cover several decades.

10-10 The internal standard method (Section 1E-3) is often used in preparing ICP calibration curves to compensate for random instrumental errors arising from fluctuations in the output of the plasma source.

CHAPTER 11

11-1 Three types of mass spectrometers have been used in atomic mass spectrometry: (1) the quadrupole mass analyzer, (2) the time-of-flight mass spectrometer, and (3) the double-focusing mass spectrometer. The quadrupole mass spectrometer separates ions of different mass based upon selective filtration of ions during their passage through four parallel rods that serve as electrodes. One pair of rods is attached to a positive variable dc voltage and the other to a negative dc voltage. In addition variable radio frequency ac potentials that are 180 deg out of phase are applied to each pair of rods. The ions to be separated are then accelerated between the rods. Depending upon the two potentials only ions having a limited range of m/z values are able to pass through the length of space between the rods, all others are annihilated by striking the rods. Thus, by varying the dc and ac potentials simultaneously, separation of ions of different masses occurs.

In a time-of-flight mass spectrometer ions are accelerated periodically into a field-free drift tube. Their velocity in the tube is determined by their mass-to-charge ratio so that they arrive at a detector at different times depending upon their mass.

In a double-focusing mass spectrometer, ions are accelerated into a curved electrostatic field and then into an electromagnetic field. The lightest ions are deflected to a greater extent than are heavier ions, and thus are dispersed on a plane where they are detected.

11-2 The torch in an ICPMS instrument causes atomization of the sample components and conversion of these atomic particles to ions that can then be separated by a mass spectrometer.

11-3 The ordinate in a mass spectrum is ordinarily the mass-to-charge ratio. The abscissa is usually the relative intensity of the ion beam.

11-4 ICPMS has become an important tool for elemental analysis because of its high sensitivity, high selectivity, and its good precision for determining most elements in the periodic table.

11-5 The interface consists of a water-cooled metal cone with a tiny orifice in its center. The region behind the cone is maintained at a pressure of about 1 torr by pumping. The hot gases from the torch impinge upon this cone and a fraction of these gases pass through the orifice where they are cooled by expansion. A fraction of the cooled gas then passes through a second orifice into a region that is maintained at the pressure of the mass spectrometer. Here, the positive analyte ions are separated from electrons and negative ions by a suitable potential and are accelerated into the mass spectrometer itself.

11-6 Lasers are used for sampling for ICPMS by exposing a solid sample to an intense, pulsed laser beam, which rapidly vaporizes the sample. The resulting vapor is then carried into the ICP torch where atomization and ionization occurs. The resulting gaseous mixture is then carried into a mass spectrometer for ion analysis.

11-7 Isobaric interferences are encountered when the isotopes of two elements have the same mass. A second type of spectroscopic interference occurs from molecular species that have the same mass as that of an analyte atom. A third type of interference is from matrix species that combine with the analyte and reduce the analyte signal as a consequence.

11-8 An internal standard is often used in preparation of calibration curves for ICPMS in order to compensate for random error from instrument drift and noise, source torch instabilities, and matrix effects. The internal standard chosen is an element that is normally absent from the sample but one that has an atomic mass and ionization potential close to that of the analyte.

11-9 In an isotope dilution experiment, a known weight of the analyte that has been prepared from a non-naturally occurring isotope of one of the elements in the analyte is added to the sample to be analyzed and mixed thoroughly until homogenization is assured. A known weight of the sample is then taken and a fraction of the highly purified analyte is isolated and weighed. The amount of enriched analyte is then determined by a mass spectrometric measurement. As shown in Section 32D-1, these data then permit the calculation of the percent analyte in the original sample.

11-10 In a glow-discharge mass spectrometric analysis, the sample is made part of the cathode of a glow-discharge atomizer, such as that shown in Figure 8-10. Here, the solid sample is bombarded by a stream of argon ions that have been accelerated through a potential of 250 to 1000 V. Analyte atoms anions are then sputtered from the sample and passed into a mass spectrometer for analysis.

11-11 In secondary-ion mass spectrometry, the sample is bombarded with a stream of 5- to 20-keV positive ions, such as Ar^+ or Cs^+. The ion beam is formed in an ion gun. The impact of the beam on the surface of the sample results in secondary ion formation containing analyte ions, which then pass into a mass spectrometer for analysis.

CHAPTER 12

12-1 $\lambda_0 = 12398/80 \times 10^3) = \underline{0.155 \text{ Å}}$ (Equation 12 – 2, page 273)

12-2 Equations 12-1 and 12-2 give the minimum voltage required to produce an emission line of wavelength λ. Thus,

$$hc/\lambda = V_{min} e$$

$$V_{min} = 12398/\lambda$$

(a) For U and $K_{\beta 1}$ and $L_{\beta 1}$ lines at 0.111 Å and 0.720 Å respectively (Table 12-1)

$K_{\beta 1}$ line	$L_{\beta 1}$ line
$V_{min} = 12398/0.111$	$V_{min} = 12398/0.720$
$= 1.12 \times 10^5$ V or $\underline{112 \text{ kV}}$	$= 1.72 \times 10^4$ V or $\underline{17.2 \text{ kV}}$

(b) For K, $V_{min} = 12398/3.454$ No $L_{\beta 1}$ line

                 $= 3589$ V or $\underline{3.59 \text{ kV}}$

(c) For Rb, $V_{min} = 12398/0.829$ $V_{min} = 12398/7.075$

                 $= 1.50 \times 10^4$ V or15.0 kV $= 1752$ V or $\underline{1.75 \text{ V}}$

(d) For W, $V_{min} = 12398/0.184$ $V_{min} = 12398/1.282$

                 $= 6.74 \times 10^4$V or $\underline{67.4 \text{ kV}}$ $= 9671$ V or $\underline{9.67 \text{ kV}}$

12-3 Here, we assume that a linear relationship exists between the atomic number Z for elements in question and the square root of the frequency ν of their K_α lines (see Figure 12-3); this linear relationship can then be used to determine the frequency and wavelength of the other elements. Thus we may write

For Ca, $Z = 20$ and $\sqrt{v} = \sqrt{3.00 \times 10^{10}/(3.36 \times 10^{-8})} = 9.5 \times 10^8$

For Zn, $Z = 30$ and $\sqrt{v} = \sqrt{3.00 \times 10^{10}/1.44 \times 10^{-8})} = 1.44 \times 10^9$

For Zr, $Z = 40$ and $\sqrt{v}\sqrt{3.00 \times 10^{10}/(0.79 \times 10^{-9})} = 1.95 \times 10^9$

For Sn, $Z = 50$ and $\sqrt{v} = \sqrt{3.00 \times 10^{10}/(0.49 \times 10^{-8})} = 2.47 \times 10^9$

A plot of these data is found at the end of this solution. From this straight line, we obtain the data in columns 3 and 4.

	Element	Z	$\sqrt{v}$	K_α λ, Å	$\sqrt{v}$	L_α λ, Å
(a)	V	23	10.9×10^8	2.5	3.5×10^8	24
(b)	Ni	28	13.5×10^8	1.6	4.6×10^8	14
(c)	Se	34	16.5×10^8	1.1	5.8×10^8	8.9
(d)	Br	35	17.0×10^8	1.0	6.0×10^8	8.3
(e)	Cd	48	23.6×10^8	0.54	$8.7 \ 10^8$	4.0
(f)	Sb	51	25.1×10^8	0.47	9.3×10^8	3.5

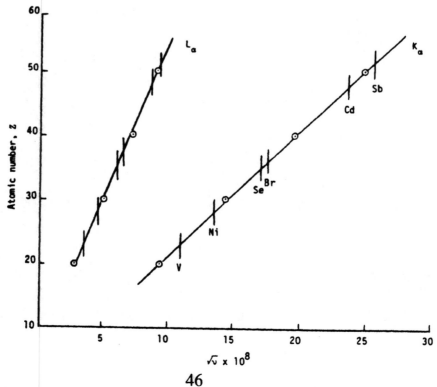

46

12-4 A plot of Z vs. $\sqrt{v}$ for the L_α lines for Ca, Zn, Zr, and Sn are shown in the figure at the end of Solution 12-3.

From this plot we obtain the data shown in columns 5 and 6 of the table in Solution 12-3.

12-5 $\ln P_0/P = \mu_M \rho x$ (Equation 12 – 3, page 277)

$$\ln(1/0.361) = 49.2\,\frac{cm^2}{g} \times 8.9\,\frac{g}{cm^3} \times x\, cm$$

$$x = 1.019/(49.2 \times 8.9) = \underline{2.3 \times 10^{-3}\, cm}$$

12-6 $\mu_M = W_K\mu_K + W_I\mu_I + W_H\mu_H + W_O\mu_O$ (Equation 12 – 4, page 278)

(a) $$\mu_M = \frac{8.00}{100}\left(\frac{39.1}{166.0} \times 16.7 + \frac{126.9}{166.0} \times 39.2\right) + \frac{92}{100}\left(0 + \frac{16.0}{18.0} \times 1.50\right)$$

$$= \underline{3.94\, cm^2/g}$$

(b) $\ln P_0/P = \mu_M \rho x = 3.94 \times 1.05 \times 0.50 = 2.069$

$P/P_0 = \underline{0.126}$

12-7 $\ln(P_0/P) = \ln(1.00/0.98) = \mu_M\rho x = 2.74 \times 2.70\, x$ (Equation 12 – 3)

$$x = 2.020/(2.74 \times 2.70) = \underline{2.73 \times 10^{-3}\, cm^{-1}}$$

12-8 $\ln(P_0/P) = \ln(100/27.3) = \mu_M\rho x = \mu_M \times 0.794 \times 1.50$ (Equation 12 – 3)

$$\mu_M = 1.30/(0.794 \times 1.500) = 1.09$$

(a) $\mu_M = 1.09 = 2 \times 39.2\, W_{I_2}$

$W_{I_2} = 0.0139$ or $\underline{1.39\%\, I_3}$

(b) $$\mu_M = 1.09 = 2 \times 39.2\, W_{I_2} + W_{ETOH}\left(\frac{24}{46} \times 0.70 + 0.00 + \frac{16}{46} \times 1.50\right)$$

$$1.09 = 78.4\, W_{I_2} + 0.887\, W_{ETOH}$$

$$1 = W_{I_2} + W_{ETOH}$$

Solving the two equations yields

$$W_{I_2} = 2.62 \times 10^{-3} \text{ or } \underline{0.262\%\, I_2}$$

12-9 $n\lambda = 2d \sin\theta$ (Equation 12 – 6, page 278)

(a) $d = 1.356$ Å   (Table 12-3)

For Fe (1.76 Å), $1 \times 1.76 = 2 \times 1.356 \sin \theta$

$\theta = 40.46$ and $2\theta = \underline{80.9 \text{ deg}}$

The following data were obtained in this same way.

	(a) Topaz ($d = 1.356$ Å)	(b) LiF ($d = 2.014$ Å)	(c) NaCl ($d = 2.820$ Å)
Fe (1.76 Å)	80.9 deg	51.8 deg	36.4 deg
Se (0.992 Å)	42.9	28.5	20.3
Ag (0.497 Å)	21.1	14.2	10.1

12-10 Employing the method used in Solution 12-9, we find

(a) $2\theta = \underline{135 \text{ deg}}$ (b) $\underline{99.5 \text{ deg}}$

12-11 $V = 12398/(\lambda \times 10^3) = $ kV   (Equation $12 - 2$)

(a) $\underline{4.046 \text{ kV}}$ (b) $\underline{1.323 \text{ kV}}$ (c) $\underline{20.94 \text{ kV}}$ (d) $\underline{25.00 \text{ kV}}$

12-12

	Count Per Second		Ratio
Wt % Mn	Ba	Mn	Mn/Ba, Counts/s
0.0500	156	80	0.513
0.150	160	106	0.663
0.250	159	129	0.811
0.350	160	154	0.963
0.450	151	167	1.106

A least-squares treatment of the data leads to the following ratio between the wt % Mn (W) and the count ratio Q.

$W = 1.49 R + 0.440$

Substituting 0.886 into this equation leads to

$W = \underline{0.300 \ (\pm 0.002) \ \% \text{ Mn}}$

CHAPTER 13

13-1 (a) $T = 100 \times \text{antilog} (-0.0510) = \underline{\underline{88.9\%}}$

Proceeding in the same way, we obtain

(b) $\underline{12.1\%}$ (c) $\underline{41.8\%}$ (d) $\underline{54.8\%}$ (e) $\underline{32.7\%}$ (f) $\underline{19.9\%}$

13-2 (a) $A = -\log (25.5/100) = \underline{0.593}$

Proceeding in the same way, we obtain

(b) $\underline{0.246}$ (c) $\underline{0.484}$ (d) $\underline{1.45}$ (e) $\underline{1.07}$ (f) $\underline{0.269}$

13-3 (a) $T = 100 \times \text{antilog} (-0.0510 \times 2) = \underline{\underline{79.1\%}}$

Similarly,

(b) $\underline{1.46\%}$ (c) $\underline{17.5\%}$ (d) $\underline{30.1\%}$ (e) $\underline{10.7\%}$ (f) $\underline{39.4\%}$

13-4 (a)
$$A = -\log \frac{0.255}{2} = \underline{0.894}$$

Similarly,

(b) $\underline{0.547}$ (c) $\underline{0.785}$ (d) $\underline{1.75}$ (e) $\underline{1.37}$ (f) $\underline{0.570}$

13-5
$$c = \frac{4.48 \text{ mg KMnO}_4}{L} \times \frac{10^{-3} \text{ g KMnO}_4}{\text{mg KMnO}_4} \times \frac{1 \text{ mol KMnO}_4}{158.03 \text{ g KMnO}_4}$$

$$= 2.835 \times 10^{-5} \frac{\text{mol KMnO}_4}{L}$$

$$A = -\log 0.309 = 0.5100$$

$$\varepsilon = \frac{0.5100}{1.00 \times 2.835 \times 10^{-5}} = \underline{\underline{1.80 \times 10^4 \text{ L cm}^{-1} \text{ mol}^{-1}}}$$

13-6
$$3.75 \frac{\text{mg}}{100 \text{ mL}} \times \frac{1 \text{ mmol A}}{220 \text{ mg A}} = 1.705 \times 10^{-4} \frac{\text{mmol A}}{\text{mL}}$$

$$A = -\log 0.396 = 0.4023$$

$$\varepsilon = 0.4023/(1.50 \times 10^{-4}) = \underline{\underline{1.57 \times 10^3}}$$

13-7 $\varepsilon = 9.32 \times 10^3 \text{ L cm}^{-1} \text{ mol}^{-1}$

(a) $A = 9.32 \times 10^3 \times 1.00 \times 6.24 \times 10^{-5} = \underline{0.582}$

(b) $T = \text{antilog}(-0.582) \times 100\% = \underline{26.2\%}$

(c) $c = A/\varepsilon b = 0.582/(9.32 \times 10^3 \times 5.00) = \underline{1.25 \times 10^{-5}\,M}$

13-8 (a) $A_1 = \varepsilon b c = 7.00 \times 10^3 \times 1.00 \times 2.50 \times 10^{-5} = \underline{0.175}$

(b) $A_2 = 2 \times A_1 = 2 \times 0.175 = \underline{0.350}$

(c) $T_1 = \text{antilog}(-0.175) = \underline{0.668}$ or $\underline{66.8\%}$

$T_2 = \text{antilog}(-0.350) = \underline{0.447}$ or $\underline{44.7\%}$

(d) $A = -\log(0.668/2) = \underline{0.476}$

13-9 $\varepsilon = 7.00 \times 10^3\,\text{L cm}^{-1}\,\text{mol}^{-1}$

$c_{Fe} = 3.8\,\dfrac{\text{mg Fe}}{\text{L}} \times 10^{-3}\,\dfrac{\text{g Fe}}{\text{mg Fe}} \times \dfrac{1\,\text{mol Fe}}{55.85\,\text{g Fe}} \times \dfrac{2.50\,\text{mL}}{50.0\,\text{mL}} = 3.40 \times 10^{-6}\,M$

$A = 7.00 \times 10^3 \times 2.50 \times 3.40 \times 10^{-6} = \underline{0.059}$

13-10 (a) $T = (\text{antilog} - 0.464) \times 100\% = \underline{34.4\%}$

(b) In 2.50-cm cell, $A = 0.464 \times 2.50/1.00 = 1.160$

$T = (\text{antilog} - 1.160) \times 100\% = \underline{6.92\%}$

(c) $c_{\text{complex}} = c_{Zn^{2+}} = 1.60 \times 10^{-4}$

$\varepsilon = \dfrac{0.464}{1.00 \times 1.60 \times 10^{-4}} = \underline{2.90 \times 10^3}$

13-11 $[H_3O^+][In^-]/[HIn] = 8.00 \times 10^{-5}$

$[H_3O^+] = [In^-];\qquad [HIn] = c_{HIn} - [In^-]$

(a) At $c_{HIn} = 3.00 \times 10^{-4}$

$\dfrac{[In^-]^2}{(3.00 \times 10^{-4}) - [In^-]} = 8.00 \times 10^{-5}$

$$[In^-]^2 + 8.00 \times 10^{-5} [In^-] - 2.40 \times 10^{-8} = 0$$

$$[In^-] = 1.20 \times 10^{-4}$$

$$[HIn] = 3.00 \times 10^{-4} - 1.20 \times 10^{-4} = 1.80 \times 10^{-4}$$

$$A_{430} = 1.20 \times 10^{-4} \times 0.775 \times 10^3 + 1.80 \times 10^{-4} \times 8.04 \times 10^3 = \underline{\underline{1.54}}$$

$$A_{600} = 1.20 \times 10^{-4} \times 6.96 \times 10^3 + 1.80 \times 10^{-4} \times 1,23 \times 10^3 = \underline{\underline{1.06}}$$

The remaining calculations are performed in the same way and yield the following results.

c_{ind}, M	$[In^-]$	$[HIn]$	A_{430}	A_{600}
3.00×10^{-4}	1.20×10^{-4}	1.80×10^{-4}	1.54	1.06
2.00×10^{-4}	9.27×10^{-5}	1.07×10^{-4}	0.935	0.777
1.00×10^{-4}	5.80×10^{-5}	4.20×10^{-5}	0.383	0.455
0.500×10^{-4}	3.48×10^{-5}	1.52×10^{-5}	0.149	0.261
0.250×10^{-4}	2.00×10^{-5}	5.00×10^{-6}	0.056	0.145

(b)

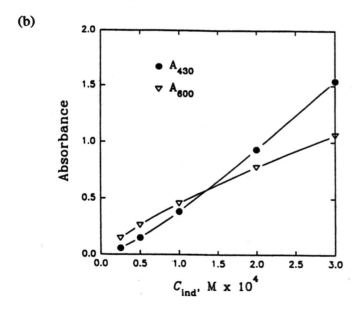

13-12 $[Cr_2O_7^{2-}]/[CrO_4^{2-}]^2[H^+]^2 = 4.2 \times 10^{14}$

$[H^+] = \text{antilog}(-5.60) = 2.51 \times 10^{-6}$

$[Cr_2O_7^{2-}] = c_{K_2Cr_2O_7} - [CrO_4^{2-}]/2$

$$\frac{c_{K_2Cr_2O_7} - [CrO_4^{2-}]/2}{[CrO_4^{2-}]^2 \times (2.51 \times 10^{-6})^2} = 4.2 \times 10^{14}$$

$c_{K_2Cr_2O_7} - 0.500[CrO_4^{2-}] = 2.65 \times 10^3 [CrO_4^{2-}]^2$

$[CrO_4^{2-}]^2 + 1.887 \times 10^{-4} [CrO_4^{2-}] - 3.774 \times 10^{-4} c_{K_2Cr_2O_7} = 0$

When $c_{K_2Cr_2O_7} = 4.00 \times 10^{-4}$

$[CrO_4^{2-}]^2 + 1.887 \times 10^{-4} [CrO_4^{2-}] - 1.510 \times 10^{-7} = 0$

$[CrO_4^{2-}] = 3.055 \times 10^{-4}$

$[Cr_2O_7^{2-}] = 4.00 \times 10^{-4} - 3.055 \times 10^{-4}/2 = 2.473 \times 10^{-4}$

$A_{345} = 1.84 \times 10^3 \times 3.055 \times 10^{-4} + 10.7 \times 10^2 \times 2.473 \times 10^{-4} = 0.826$

$A_{370} = 4.81 \times 10^3 \times 3.055 \times 10^{-4} + 7.28 \times 10^2 \times 2.473 \times 10^{-4} = 1.649$

$A_{400} = 1.88 \times 10^3 \times 3.055 \times 10^{-4} + 1.89 \times 10^2 \times 2.473 \times 10^{-4} = 0.621$

Proceeding in the same way, we obtain

$c_{K_2Cr_2O_7}$	$[CrO_4^{2-}]$	$[Cr_2O_7^{2-}]$	A_{345}	A_{370}	A_{400}
4.00×10^{-4}	3.055×10^{-4}	2.473×10^{-4}	0.826	1.649	0.621
3.00×10^{-4}	2.551×10^{-4}	1.725×10^{-4}	0.654	1.352	0.512
2.00×10^{-4}	1.961×10^{-4}	1.019×10^{-4}	0.470	1.018	0.388
1.00×10^{-4}	1.216×10^{-4}	3.920×10^{-5}	0.266	0.613	0.236

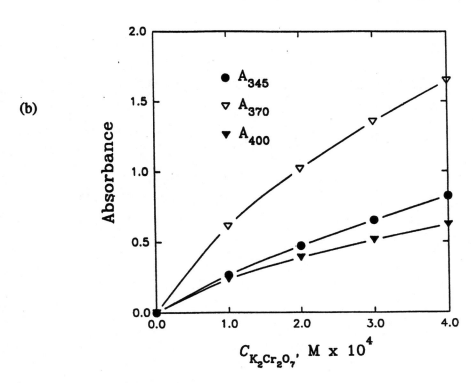

(b)

13-13 (a) *Hydrogen and deuterium lamps* differ only in the gases they contain. The latter produces radiation of somewhat higher intensity.

(b) *Filters* provide low resolution wavelength selection often suitable for quantitative work but not for qualitative analysis. *Monochromators* produce high resolution (narrow bandwidths) for both qualitative and quantitative work.

(c) A *phototube* is a vacuum tube equipped with a photoemissive cathode. It has a high electrical resistance and requires a potential of 90 V or more to produce a photocurrent. The currents are generally small enough to require considerable amplification before they can be measured. A *photovoltaic cell* consists of a photo-sensitive semiconductor sandwiched between two electrodes. A current is generated between the electrodes when radiation is absorbed by the semiconducting layer. The current is generally large enough to be measured directly with a microammeter. The advantages of a phototube are greater sensitivity and wave-length range as well as better reproducibility. The advantages of the photocell are its simplicity, low cost, and general ruggedness. In addition, it does not require an external power supply or elaborate electric circuitry. Its use is limited to visible radiation, however, and in addition it suffers from fatigue whereby its electrical output decreases gradually with time.

(d) *Phototubes* consist of a single photoemissive surface (cathode) and an anode in an evacuated envelope. They exhibit low dark current but have no inherent amplification (gain). *Photomultipliers* have built-in gain but suffer from somewhat larger dark current.

(e) A *photometer* is an instrument for absorption measurements that consists of a source, a filter, and a photoelectric detector. A *colorimeter* differs from a photometer in the respect that the human eye serves as the detector. The photometer offers the advantage of greater precision and the ability to discriminate between color. The main advantages of a colorimeter are simplicity, low cost, and the fact that no power supply is needed.

(f) *Spectrophotometers* have monochromators for multiple wavelength operation and for procuring spectra while *photometers* utilize filters for fixed wavelength operation.

(g) A *single-beam spectrophotometer* employs a fixed beam of radiation that irradiates first the solvent and then the analyte solution. In a *double-beam instrument*, the solvent and solution are irradiated simultaneously or nearly so. The advantages of the double-beam instruments are freedom from problems arising from fluctuations in the source intensity from drift in electronic circuits; in addition, it is more easily adapted to automatic spectral recording. The single-beam instrument offers the advantages of simplicity and lower cost.

(h) Diode array spectrometers detect the entire spectral range essentially simultaneously and can produce a spectrum in less than a second. *Spectrometers* require several minutes to perform the same task. Accordingly the diode array instruments can be used to monitor processes that occur on very fast time scales. Conventional spectrometers require several minutes to perform the same task.

13-14 (a) $\%\,T = P/P_0 \times 100\% = I/I_0 \times 100\%$

$$= 24.9\,\mu A / 73.6\,\mu A \times 100\% = \underline{\underline{33.8\%}}$$

(b) $A = -\log T = -\log 24.9/73.6 = \underline{0.471}$

(c) $A = \varepsilon bc \qquad 1/3\,A = \varepsilon bc/3$

$A_{1/3} = (0.471)/3 = 0.157$

$T = 10^{-0.157} = \underline{0.697}$

(d) $A_2 = 2A = 2(0.471) = 0.942$

$T = 10^{-0.942} = \underline{0.114} \quad \text{or} \quad 11.4\%$

13-15 (a) $T = 179\,mV / 685\,mV = \underline{0.261}$

$A = -\log T = -\log 0.261 = \underline{0.583}$

(b) $A = 0.583/2 = \underline{0.291}$

$T = 10^{-0.291} = \underline{0.511}$

(c) $A = 2 \times 0.583 = 1.166$

$T = 10^{-1.166} = \underline{0.0682}$

13-16 In a *deuterium lamp*, the input energy from the power source produces an excited deuterium molecule that dissociates into two atoms in the ground state and a photon of radiation. As the excited deuterium molecule relaxes, its quantized energy is distributed between the energy of the photon and the kinetic energies of the two deuterium atoms. The later can vary from nearly zero to the original energy of the excited molecule. Therefore, the energy of the radiation, which is the difference between the quantized energy of the excited molecule and the kinetic energies of the atoms, can also vary continuously over the same range. Consequently, the emission spectrum is a continuum.

13-17 A *photon detector* produces a current or voltage as a result of the emission of electrons from a photosensitive surface upon collision with photons. On the other hand, a *heat detector* consists of a darkened surface to absorb infrared energy to produce a temperature increase and a thermal transducer to produce an electrical signal whose magnitude is related to the temperature and thus the intensity of the infrared energy.

13-18 The power of an infrared beam is measured with a heat detector, which consists of a tiny blackened surface that is warmed as a consequence of radiation absorption. This surface is attached to a transducer, which converts the heat signal to an electrical one. Heat transducers are of three types: (1) a *thermopile*, which consists of several dissimilar metal junctions that develop a potential that depends upon the difference in temperature of the junctions; (2) a *bolometer*, which is fashioned from a conductor whose electrical resistance depends upon temperature; and (3) a *pneumatic detector* whose internal pressure is temperature-dependent.

13-19 Photons from the infrared region of the spectrum do not have sufficient energy to cause photoemission from the cathode of a photomultiplier.

13-20 *Tungsten/halogen lamps* contain a small amount of iodine in the evacuated quartz envelope that contains the tungsten filament. The iodine prolongs the life of the lamp and permits it to operate at a higher temperature. The iodine combines with gaseous tungsten that sublimes from the filament and causes the metal to be redeposited, thus adding to the life of the lamp.

13-21 Basically an *absorption photometer* and a *fluorescence photometer* consist of the same components. The basic difference is in the location of the detector. The detector in a fluorometer is positioned at an angle of 90 deg to the direction of the beam from the source so that emission is detected rather than transmission. In addition, a filter is often positioned in form of detector to remove radiation from the excitation beam that may result from scattering or other nonfluorescence processes. In a transmission photometer, the detector is positioned in a line with the source, the filter, and the detector.

13-22 The basic difference between an *absorption spectrometer* and an *emission spectrometer* is that the former requires a separate radiation source and a sample compartment that holds containers for the sample and its solvent. With an emission spectrometer, the sample container is a hot flame, a heated surface, or an electric arc or spark that also serves as the radiation source.

13-23 The performance characteristics of an interference filter include the wavelength of its transmittance peak, the percent transmission at the peak, and the effective bandwidth.

13-24 (a) The *dark current* is the small current that develops in a radiation transducer in the absence of radiation.

(b) A *transducer* is a device that converts a physical or chemical quantity into an electrical signal.

(c) *Scattered radiation* in a monochromator is unwanted radiation that reaches the exit slit as a result of reflection and scattering. Its wavelength is usually different from that of the radiation reaching the slit directly from the dispersing element.

(d) An *n-type semiconductor* is a material consisting of silicon or germanium that has been doped with an element from Group 5A of the periodic table to impart extra electrons into the crystal lattice of the semiconducting element. These electrons become the mobile charge carriers when the material passes a current.

(e) The *majority carrier* in a semiconductor is the mobile charge carrier in either *n*-type or *p*-type semiconductors. For *n*-type, the majority carrier is the electron while in *p*-type, the majority carrier is a positively charged hole.

(f) A *depletion layer* in a *pn* junction appears when the diode is operated under reverse-bias conditions. Here the region between the electrodes is depleted of positive and negative charges so that it is nonconducting.

13-25 (a)

$$\lambda_{max} = 2t\eta/n \qquad t = \frac{\lambda_{max}/n}{2\eta}$$

$$t = \frac{4.54 \ \mu m \ (1)}{2(1.34)} = \underline{\underline{1.69 \ \mu m}}$$

(b) $\lambda_n = (2t\eta)/n$

For $n = 1, 2, 3, \cdots$

$$\lambda_1 = 2t\eta = \underline{\underline{4.54 \ \mu m}}$$

$$\lambda_2 = 1/2\lambda_1 = \underline{\underline{2.27 \ \mu m}}$$

$$\lambda_3 = 1/3 \lambda_1 = \underline{\underline{1.51 \ \mu m}} \qquad (etc.)$$

13-26 The effective bandwidth of a filter is the width in wavelength units of the band transmitted by the filter when measured at one half the peak height.

13-27 $n\lambda = d(\sin i + \sin r)$ (Equation $7 - 6$)

$d = n\lambda/(\sin i + \sin r) = 1 \times 500/(\sin 60 + \sin 10)$

$= 500/0.866 + 0.174) = 481 nm$

$$line/mm = \frac{1 \ line}{481 \ nm} \times 10^6 \frac{mm}{nm} = 2079$$

13-28 $n\lambda = d(\sin i + \sin r)$ (Equation 7 – 6)

$d = 1 \text{ mm}/72 \text{ lines} = 0.01389 \text{ mm/line} = 13.9 \text{ μm/line}$

(a) For $n = 1$ and $\sin i = 0$

$$\lambda = 13.9(\sin 50 + \sin 0) = 10.65 \text{ μm}$$

For $n = 2$ $\lambda = 5.32 \text{ μm}$

(b) For $n = 1$ $\lambda = 13.9(\sin 50 + \sin 15) = 14.25 \text{ μm}$

For $n = 2$ $\lambda = 7.12$

13-29 (a) A spectroscope consists of a monochromator with an eyepiece that moves along the focal plane. The angle between the incident and dispersed beam is a function of wavelength. A spectroscope is used for the visual identification of atomic emission lines.

(b) A spectrograph is a monochromator with a film or photographic plate located along its focal plane for photographic recording of spectra.

(c) A spectrophotometer is a monochromator with a photodetector located at its exit slit. Provision is made for moving the dispersing element so various portions of the spectrum can be focused on the slit.

13-30 Quantitative analyses can tolerate rather wide slits since measurements are usually carried out at maxima where the slope of the spectrum $dA/d\lambda$ is relatively constant. On the other hand, qualitative analyses require narrow slits so that any fine structure in the spectrum will be resolved.

CHAPTER 14

14-1 (a) A plot of the data reveals a linear relationship between absorbance and ppm Fe.

(b) Proceeding as in Example a1-12, Appendix 1, we write

$c_{Fe} = x_i$	$A = y_i$	x_i^2	y_i^2	$x_i y_i$
2.00	0.164	4.00	0.026896	0.328
5.00	0.425	25.00	0.180625	2.125
8.00	0.628	64.00	0.394384	5.024
12.00	0.951	144.00	0.994401	11.412
16.00	1.260	256.00	1.587600	20.160
20.00	1.582	400.00	2.502724	31.640
$\sum x_i = 63.00$	$\sum y_i = 5.010$	$\sum x_i^2 = 893.00$	$\sum y_i^2 = 5.596630$	$\sum y_i^2 = 70.689$

$$S_{xx} = 893.00 - (63.00)^2/6 = 231.50$$

$$S_{yy} = 5.596630 - (5.010)^2/6 = 1.41328$$

$$S_{xy} = 70.689 - (63.00 \times 5.00)/6 = 18.084$$

$$m = 18.084/231.50 = 0.0781163 = 0.0781$$

$$b = \frac{5.010}{6} - 0.078117 \times \frac{63.00}{6} = 0.01477$$

$$y = \underline{0.0781\,x + 0.0148}$$

(c)
$$s_y = \sqrt{\frac{1.41328 - (0.078117)^2\,231.50}{6 - 2}} = \underline{\underline{1.23 \times 10^{-2}}}$$

(d) $s_m = 1.23 \times 10^{-2}/\sqrt{231.50} = \underline{\underline{8.1 \times 10^{-4}}}$

14-2 (a) Substituting into the equation developed in Solution 14-1b, we obtain

$$0.107 = 0.0781\,x + 0.0148$$

$$x = c_{Fe} = \underline{\underline{1.18\ ppm\ Fe}}$$

For 1 measurement

$$s_x = \frac{1.23 \times 10^{-2}}{0.0781}\sqrt{\frac{1}{1} + \frac{1}{6} + \frac{(0.107 - 5.01/6)^2}{(0.0781)^2 \times 231.50}} = \underline{\underline{0.20\ ppm\ Fe}}$$

For mean of 3 measurements

$$s_x = \frac{1.23 \times 10^{-2}}{0.0781}\sqrt{\frac{1}{3} + \frac{1}{6} + \frac{(0.107 - 5.01/6)^2}{(0.0781)^2 \times 231.5}} = \underline{\underline{0.15\ ppm\ Fe}}$$

Proceeding in the same way, we compute

(b) $c_{Fe} = \underline{\underline{9.04\ ppm}}$, $(s_c)_1 = \underline{\underline{0.17\ ppm}}$, and $(s_c)_3 = \underline{\underline{0.11\ ppm}}$

(c) $c_{Fe} = \underline{\underline{19.50\ ppm}}$, $(s_c)_1 = \underline{\underline{0.20\ ppm}}$, and $(s_c)_3 = \underline{\underline{0.15\ ppm}}$

14-3 Proceeding as in Example 13-1 (page 304) we obtain the general relationships

$$[In^-]^2 + 1.42 \times 10^{-5}\,[In^-] - 1.42 \times 10^{-5} \times c_{HIn} = 0$$

$$[In^-] = \frac{-1.42 \times 10^{-5} + \sqrt{2.016 \times 10^{-10} + 5.68 \times 10^{-5}\,c_{HIn}}}{2}$$

Substituting the various concentrations of c_{HIn} in column 1 of Table 13-2 yields the data for [In⁻] in column 3. To obtain the data in column 2, we write

$$[\text{HIn}] = c_{HIn} - [\text{In}^-]$$

For example, solving the quadratic for $c_{HIn} = 4.00 \times 10^{-5}$ gives

$$[\text{In}^-] = 1.78 \times 10^{-5} \quad \text{and}$$

$$[\text{HIn}] = 4.00 \times 10^{-5} - 1.78 \times 10^{-5} = 2.22 \times 10^{-5}$$

We then write

$$A_{430} = 2.06 \times 10^4 \, [\text{In}^-] + 6.30 \times 10^2 \, [\text{HIn}]$$

$$A_{570} = 9.61 \times 10^2 \, [\text{In}^-] + 7.12 \times 10^3 \, [\text{HIn}]$$

Thus

$$A_{430} = 2.06 \times 10^4 \times 1.78 \times 10^{-5} + 6.30 \times 10^2 \times 2.22 \times 10^{-5} = 0.381$$

$$A_{570} = 9.61 \times 10^2 \times 1.78 \times 10^{-5} + 7.12 \times 10^3 \times 2.22 \times 10^{-5} = 0.175$$

The remainder of the data in the table can be confirmed in this same way.

14-4 Letting the subscripts x and s refer to the unknown and standard solutions respectively and V_t be the total volume of solution, we may write

$$A_x = \varepsilon b c_x V_x / V_t$$

$$A_s = \varepsilon b \, (c_x V_x + c_s V_s)/V_t$$

Dividing the first equation by the second and rearranging gives

$$c_x = \frac{A_x c_s V_s}{(A_s - A_x) V_x} = \frac{0.832 \times 23.4 \times 10.0}{(1.220 - 0.832) \, 25.0} = \underline{20.1 \text{ ppm}}$$

14-5 Using equation developed in Solution 14-4

$$c_{Cu^{2+}} = \frac{0.512 \times 3.82 \times 4.00}{(0.844 - 0.512) \times 50.0} = 0.4713 \text{ ppm Cu}$$

Recall that for dilute aqueous solutions, 1 ppm = 1 mg/L.

$$\% \text{Cu} = 200 \text{ mL} \times 0.4713 \frac{\text{mg}}{\text{L}} \times \frac{10^{-3} \text{ g}}{\text{mg}} \times \frac{\text{L}}{10^3 \text{ mL}} \times \frac{1}{5.12 \text{ g}} \times 100\% = \underline{1.84 \times 10^{-3}}$$

14-6 (a) $A_{365} = 0.598 = 3529 \times 1.00 \times c_{Co} + 3228 \times 1.00\, c_{Ni}$

$A_{700} = 0.039 = 428.9 \times 1.00 \times c_{Co} + 10.2 \times 1.00\, c_{Ni}$

Rearranging the second equation gives

$$c_{Co} = (0.039 - 10.2\, c_{Ni})/428.9$$

$$= 9.09 \times 10^{-5} - 2.378 \times 10^{-3} \times c_{Ni}$$

Substituting into the first equation gives

$$0.598 = 3529(9.09 \times 10^{-5} - 2.378 \times 10^{-2}\, c_{Ni}) + 3228\, c_{Ni}$$

$$0.598 = 0.3208 - 83.9\, c_{Ni} + 3228\, c_{Ni}$$

$$c_{Ni} = \underline{\underline{8.82 \times 10^{-5}\, M}}$$

Substituting into the first equation gives

$$c_{Co} = \frac{0.598 - 3228 \times 8.82 \times 10^{-5}}{3529} = \underline{\underline{8.88 \times 10^{-5}\, M}}$$

(b) Proceeding in the same way, we obtain

$$c_{Ni} = \underline{\underline{9.8 \times 10^{-5}\, M}} \quad \text{and} \quad c_{Co} = \underline{\underline{1.66 \times 10^{-4}\, M}}$$

14-7 At 475 nm, $\varepsilon_A = 0.129/8.50 \times 10^{-5} = 1518$

$$\varepsilon_B = 0.567/4.65 \times 10^{-5} = 12,194$$

At 700 nm, $\varepsilon_A = 0.764/8.50 \times 10^{-5} = 8988$

$$\varepsilon_B = 0.083/4.65 \times 10^{-5} = 1785$$

(a) $1518[A] + 12194[B] = 0.502/1.25 = 0.402$

$8988[A] + 1785[B] = 0.912/1.25 = 0.730$

Solving the two simultaneous equations gives

$$[A] = \underline{\underline{7.66 \times 10^{-5}\, M}} \quad \text{and} \quad [B] = \underline{\underline{2.34 \times 10^{-5}\, M}}$$

(b) In the same way

$$[A] = \underline{\underline{5.45 \times 10^{-5}}} \quad \text{and} \quad [B] = \underline{\underline{3.75 \times 10^{-5}}}$$

14-8 (a) At 485 nm, ε_{In} = $0.052/5.00 \times 10^{-4}$ = $\underline{104}$

ε_{HIn} = $0.454/5.00 \times 10^{-4}$ = $\underline{908}$

At 625 nm, ε_{In} = $0.823/5.00 \times 10^{-4}$ = $\underline{1646}$

ε_{HIn} = $0.176/5.00 \times 10^{-4}$ = $\underline{352}$

(b) To obtain $[In^-]$ and $[HIn]$, we write

$104 [In^-] + 908 [HIn] = 0.472$

$1646 [In^-] + 352 [HIn] = 0.351$

Solving these simultaneous equations gives

$[In^-] 1.05 \times 10^{-4} M$ and $[HIn]$ = $5.08 \times 10^4 M$

In addition, $[H^+] = 1.00 \times 10^{-5}$ and

$$K_a = \frac{[H^+][In^-]}{[HIn]} = \frac{1.00 \times 10^{-5} \times 1.05 \times 10^{-4}}{5.08 \times 10^{-4}} = \underline{\underline{2.07 \times 10^{-6}}}$$

(c) $104 [In^-] + 908 [HIn] = 0.530$

$1646 [In^-] + 352 [HIn] = 0.216$

Solving these equations gives

$[In^-]$ = $6.56 \times 10^{-6} M$ and $[HIn]$ = 5.83×10^{-4}

$$\frac{[H^+] \times 6.56 \times 10^{-6}}{5.83 \times 10^{-4}} = \underline{\underline{2.07 \times 10^{-6}}}$$

$[H^+]$ = 1.84×10^{-4}

pH = $-\log 1.84 \times 10^{-4}$ = $\underline{3.735}$

(d) $104 [In^-] + 908 [HIn] = 0.306$

$1646 [In^-] + 352 [Hin] = 0.555$

Solving these equations gives

$[In^-]$ = $2.72 \times 10^{-4} M$ and $[HIn]$ = $3.06 \times 10^{-4} M$

We then calculate $[H^+]$

$$\frac{[H^+] \times 2.27 \times 10^{-4}}{3.06 \times 10^{-4}} = 2.07 \times 10^{-6}$$

$$[H^+] = 2.33 \times 10^{-6} \quad \text{and} \quad pH = 5.633$$

In the half neutralized solution of HX, we assume that $[HX] = X^-]$ and

$$\frac{[H^+][X^-]}{[HX]} = K_a = \underline{\underline{2.33 \times 10^{-6}}}$$

(e) At $[H^+] = 1.000 \times 10^{-6}$

$$[In^-]/[HIn] = 2.07 \times 10^{-6} / 1.00 \times 10^{-6} = 2.07$$

But

$$[In^-] + [HIn] = 2.00 \times 10^{-4}$$

$$2.07\,[HIn] + [HIn] = 2.00 \times 10^{-4}$$

$$[HIn] = 6.51 \times 10^{-5}\,M$$

$$[In^-] = 2.00 \times 10^{-4} - 6.51 \times 10^{-5} = 1.35 \times 10^4\,M$$

$$A_{475} = 104 \times 1.25 \times 1.35 \times 10^{-4} + 908 \times 1.25 \times 6.51 \times 10^{-5} = \underline{0.091}$$

$$A_{625} = 1646 \times 1.25 \times 1.35 \times 10^{-4} + 352 \times 1.25 \times 6.51 \times 10^{-5} = \underline{0.306}$$

14-9 $\quad \dfrac{s_c}{c} = \dfrac{0.434}{\log T} \times \dfrac{s_T}{T} \quad$ (Equation 13 – 13, page 307)

(a) $A = 0.585$; $\ T = $ antilog $(-0.585) = 0.260$

$$\frac{s_c}{c} = \frac{0.434}{\log 0.260} \times \frac{(\pm 0.005)}{0.260} = \pm 0.014 \quad \text{or} \quad \underline{\underline{1.4\%}}$$

Proceeding in this same way, we obtain

(b) $\pm 1.4\%$ (c) $\pm 7.6\%$ (d) $\pm 3.0\%$ (e) $\pm 67\%$ (f) $\pm 40\%$

14-10 (a) Until the equivalence point, the absorbance would increase linearly with volume of reagent. Beyond equivalence, the absorbance would be approximately constant.

(b) Same as part (a).

(c) Until the equivalence point, the absorbance would decrease linearly with volume of reagent. Beyond equivalence, the absorbance would be constant and approximately zero.

(d) Same as part (a).

14-11 If a small amount of Cu^{2+} is added to the analyte solution, no absorption will occur until all of the Fe^{3+} has been used up forming the more stable Y^{4-} complex. After the equivalence point, the absorbance will increase linearly until the Cu^{2+} is used up.

14-12 $\varepsilon = 0.690/2.30 \times 10^{-4} = 3.00 \times 10^3$

$$[CuA_2^{2-}] = 0.540/3.00 \times 10^3 = 1.80 \times 10^{-4}\,M$$

$$[Cu^{2+}] = 2.30 \times 10^{-4} - 1.80 \times 10^{-4} = 0.50 \times 10^{-4}\,M$$

$$[A^{2-}] = 5.00 \times 10^{-4} - 2 \times 1.80 \times 10^{-4} = 1.40 \times 10^{-4}\,M$$

$$K_f = \frac{[CuA_2^{2+}]}{[Cu^{2+}][A^{2+}]^2} = \frac{1.80 \times 10^{-4}}{0.50 \times 10^{-4}(1.40 \times 10^{-4})^2} = \underline{\underline{1.84 \times 10^8}}$$

14-13 $\varepsilon = 0.765/2.50 \times 10^{-4} = 3.06 \times 10^3$

$$[NiB_2^{2+}] = 0.360/3.06 \times 10^3 = 1.18 \times 10^{-4}$$

$$[Ni^{2+}] = 2.50 \times 10^{-4} - 1.18 \times 10^4 = 1.32 \times 10^{-4}$$

$$[B] = 1.00 \times 10^{-3} - 2 \times 1.18 \times 10^{-4} = 7.64 \times 10^{-4}$$

$$K_f = \frac{[NiB_2^{2+}]}{[Ni^{2+}][B]^2} = \frac{1.18 \times 10^{-4}}{1.32 \times 10^{-4}(7.64 \times 10^{-4})^2} = \underline{\underline{1.53 \times 10^6}}$$

CHAPTER 15

15-1 (a) *Fluorescence* is the process in which a molecule, excited by the absorption of radiation, emits a photon while descending from an excited electronic state to a lower state of the same spin multiplicity (that is, a singlet $\rightarrow$ singlet transition).

(b) *Phosphorescence* is the process in which a molecule, excited by the absorption of radiation, emits a photon while descending from an excited electronic state to a lower state of different spin multiplicity (that is triplet $\rightarrow$ single transition).

(c) *Resonance fluorescence* is observed when an excited species emits radiation of the same frequency as that used to cause the excitations.

(d) A *singlet state* is one in which the spins of the electrons of an atom or molecule are all paired so there is no net spin angular momentum.

(e) A *triplet state* is one in which the electrons of an atom or molecule are unpaired so that their angular moments add to give a net non-zero moment.

(f) *Vibrational relaxation* is the radiationless process by which a molecule descends to a lower electronic state without emitting radiation.

(g) *Internal conversion* is the intermolecular process in which a molecule crosses to a lower electronic state without emitting radiation.

(h) *External conversion* is a radiationless process in which a molecule falls to a lower electronic state while transferring energy to the solvent or other solutes.

(i) *Intersystem crossing* refers to the process in which a molecule in one spin state changes to a different spin state (for example, single → triplet) with nearly the same total energy. (See the horizontal arrow at the upper right side of Figure 15-1.)

(j) *Predissociation* occurs when a molecule change from a higher electronic state to an upper vibrational level of a lower electronic state in which the vibration energy is great enough to produce bond breaking.

(k) *Dissociation* occurs when radiation promotes a molecule directly up to a state with sufficiently high vibrational energy for a bond to break.

(l) *Quantum yield* is the fraction of excited molecules undergoing the process of interest. For example, the quantum yield for phosphorescence is the fraction of all molecules which have absorbed radiation that go on to phosphoresce.

(m) *Chemiluminescence* is a process by which radiation is produced as a consequence of a chemical reaction.

15-2 In a fluorescence spectrum, the exciting wavelength is held constant and the emission is measured as a function of wavelength. In an excitation spectrum, the emission is measured at one wavelengthwhile the exciting wavelength is varied. The excitation spectrum more closely resembles an absorption spectrum since the emission intensity is usually proportional to the absorbance of the molecule.

15-3 For spectrofluorometry, the analytical signal F is given by $F = 2.3\,K'\varepsilon c\,P_0$. The magnitude of F, and thus, sensitivity, can be enhanced by increasing the source intensity P_0 or the transducer sensitivity.

For spectrophotometry, the analytical signal A is given by $A = \log P_0/P$. Increasing P_0 or the detector's response to P_0 is accompanied by a corresponding increase in P. Thus, the ratio does not change nor does the analytical signal. Consequently, no improvement in sensitivity accompanies these measurements.

15-4 Fluorescein is more rigid than phenolphthalein, which leads to stronger fluorescence.

15-5 The fluorescence should be greatest in 1-chloropropane. The bromine and iodine atoms of the other solvents promotes intersystem crossing ("the heavy atom effect") and decreases the population of the S_1 state.

15-6 (a) A plot of the data reveals a linear relationship between relative intensity and μmol NADH/L.

(b) Proceeding as in Example a1-12 (Appendix 1), we obtain

x_i (μ mol/L)	x_i^2	y_i	y_i^2	$x_i y_i$
0.100	0.010000	2.24	5.0176	0.224
0.200	0.040000	4.74	22.4676	0.948
0.300	0.09000	6.59	43.4281	1.977
0.400	0.16000	8.98	80.6404	3.592
0.500	0.25000	10.93	119.4649	5.465
0.600	0.3600	14.01	196.2801	8.406
0.700	0.4900	15.49	239.9401	10.843
0.800	0.04000	18.02	324.7204	45.871

$\sum x_i = 3.600 \qquad \sum x_i^2 = 2.040 \qquad \sum y_i = 81.00 \qquad \sum y_i^2 = 1031.9592 \qquad \sum x_i y_i = 45.871$

$$S_{xx} = \sum x_i^2 - (\sum x_i)^2/N = 2.040 - (3.6)^2/8 = 0.4200$$

$$S_{yy} = \sum y_i^2 - (\sum y_i)^2/N = 1031.9592 - 820.125 = 211.8342$$

$$S_{xy} = \sum x_i y_i - (\sum x_i \sum y_i)^2/8 = 45.871 - 3/6 \times 81.0/8 = 0.421$$

$$m = 9.421/0.4200 = 22.431$$

$$b = \frac{81.0}{8} - 22.431 \times \frac{3.6}{8} = 0.03107$$

$$y = 22.431x + 0.3107$$

where y = relative intensity and x = μmol/L of NADH.

(c)

$$s_y = \sqrt{\frac{211.8342 - (22.431)^2 \times 0.4200}{8-2}} = 0.292 = 0.29$$

$$s_m = 0.292/\sqrt{0.420} = 0.45$$

$$s_b = 0.292\sqrt{\frac{2.040}{8 \times 2.040 - (3.60)^2}} = 0.2275 = 0.23$$

(d) $12.16 = 22.431x + 0.03107$

$x = 0.541$ μmol NADH

(e)
$$(s_c)_1 = \frac{0.292}{22.431} \sqrt{\frac{1}{1} + \frac{1}{8} + \frac{(12.16 - 81/8)^2}{(22.431)^2 \times 0.420}} = 0.014$$

(f)
$$(s_c)_2 = \frac{0.292}{22.431} \sqrt{\frac{1}{3} + \frac{1}{8} + \frac{(12.16 - 81/8)^2}{(22.431)^2 \times 0.420}} = 0.009$$

15-7 (a) A plot of the data shows a linear relationship between the fluorometer reading R and the volume of the standard V_s.

(b) Proceeding as in solution to Problem 15-6, we obtain

$$m = 0.9702$$

$$b = 6.131$$

$$R = 0.970 V_s + 6.13$$

(c) $s_y = 0.336$

$$s_m = 0.0300$$

$$s_b = 0.281$$

(d)
$$c_{Zn^{2+}} = \frac{b\, c_s}{m\, V_x} \qquad \text{(Equation } 1-11, \text{ page 16)}$$

where $c_{Zn^{2+}}$ is the concentration of Zn^2 in the standard solution (1.10 ppm Zn^{2+}) and V_x is the volume of the analyte solution taken.

$$c_{Zn^{2+}} = \frac{6.131}{0.9702} \times \frac{1.10}{5.00} = 1.39 \text{ ppm } Zn^{2+}$$

(e)
$$s_{c_{Zn^{2+}}} = 1.39 \sqrt{\left(\frac{0.030}{0.9702}\right)^2 + \left(\frac{0.281}{6.131}\right)^2} = 0.077 \text{ ppm } Zn^{2+}$$

15-8 (a) The fluoride ion reacts with and decompose the fluorescent complex to give nonfluorescing products. Thus, if we symbolize the complex as AlG_x^{3+}, we may write

$$\underset{\text{fluorescent}}{AlG_x^{3+}} + 6F^- \underset{\leftarrow}{\overset{\rightarrow}{}} \underset{\text{nonfluorescent}}{AlF_6^{3-}} + \underset{\text{nonfluorescent}}{xG}$$

Proceeding as in the solution to Problem 15-7 for the standard addition method, we write with the aid of Equation 1-13, page 17

$$F = \frac{k V_x c_x}{V_t} - \frac{k V_s c_s}{V_t}$$

66

Here, the minus sign arises because F *reduces* the fluorescent intensity. A plot of F against the volume of standard V_s is a straight line having a slope of m

$$m = \frac{-kc_s}{V_t}$$

and an intercept b of

$$b = kV_xc_x/V_t$$

Combining these equations gives

$$c_s = -\frac{bc_s}{mV_x}$$

which is analogous to Equation 1-11, page 16.

(b) A plot of the meter reading R versus the volume of standard V_s is a straight line with a negative slope.

(c) Proceeding as in Example a1-12, Appendix 1, we obtain

$$m = -8.96$$

$$b = 66.51$$

$$y = -8.96x + 66.51 = R = -8.96\,V_x + 66.51$$

(d) $s_m = 0.198;\qquad s_y = 0.664;\qquad s_b = 0.556$

(e)
$$c_x = -\frac{bc_s}{mV_x} = -\frac{66.51 \times 10.0}{-8.96 \times 5.00} = 14.8\ \text{ppb F}^-$$

(f)
$$s_{c_x} = c_x\sqrt{\left(\frac{s_m}{m}\right)^2 + \left(\frac{s_b}{b}\right)^2}$$

$$= 14.8\sqrt{\left(\frac{0.198}{-8.96}\right)^2 + \left(\frac{0.556}{66.51}\right)^2} = 0.35\ \text{ppb F}^-$$

15-9 Assume that the luminescent intensity L, is proportional to c_x, the concentration of iron in the original sample. Then

$$L_1 = kc_xV_x/V_t$$

where V_x and V_t are the volume of sample and volume of final solution; k is a proportionality constant.

For the solution after addition of V_s mL of standard having a concentration of c_s, the luminescent L_2 is given by

$$L_2 = kc_x V_x / V_t + kc_s V_x / V_t$$

Dividing the second equation by the first yields with rearrangement

$$c_x = \frac{L_1 c_s V_s}{(L_2 - L_1) V_x}$$

$$= \frac{16.1 \times 4.75 \times 10^{-5} \times 1.00}{(29.6 - 16.1) 2.00} = \underline{\underline{2.83 \times 10^{-5} \, M}}$$

15-10 Assume that the luminescent intensity L is proportional to the partial pressure of S_2^*. Then we may write

$$L = k[S_2^*] \quad \text{and} \quad K = [S_2^*][H_2O]^4 / ([SO_2]^2 [H_2]^4)$$

where the bracketed terms are all partial pressures and k and K are constants. The two equations can be combined to give upon rearrangement

$$[SO_2] = ([H_2O]^2 / [H_2]^2)(L/kK)^{1/2}$$

In a hydrogen-rich flame, the pressure of H_2O and H_2 should be more or less constant. Thus,

$$\underline{\underline{[SO_2] = k' L^{1/2}}}$$

15-11 The fluorescent center is the rigid quinoline ring, which is rich in π electrons.

CHAPTER 16

16-1 (a) $\nu = 3.00 \times 10^{10} \, \text{cm s}^{-1} \times 2170 \, \text{m}^{-1} = 6.51 \times 10^{13} \, \text{s}^{-4}$

$$\nu = \frac{1}{2\pi} \sqrt{\frac{k}{\mu}} \quad \text{(Equation 16 – 13, page 386)}$$

$$k = (2\pi\nu)^2 \mu = (2\pi\nu)^2 \frac{m_1 m_2}{m_1 + m_2} \quad \text{(see Equation 16 – 8)}$$

$$m_1 = \frac{12 \times 10^{-3} \, (\text{kg C/mol C})}{6.02 \times 10^{23} \, (\text{atom C/mol C})} = 1.99 \times 10^{-26} \, \text{kg C/atom C}$$

$$m_2 = \frac{16.0 \times 10^{-3} \text{ (kg O/mol O)}}{6.02 \times 10^{23} \text{ (atom O/mol O)}} = 2.66 \times 10^{-26} \text{ kg O/atom O}$$

$$k = (2\pi\nu s^{-1})^2 \times \frac{1.99 \times 10^{-26} \text{ kg} \times 2.66 \times 10^{-26}}{1.99 \times 10^{-26} \text{ kg} + 2.66 \times 10^{-26} \text{ kg}}$$

$$= (2\pi \times 6.51 \ 10^{13} \text{ s}^{-1})^2 \ 1.14 \times 10^{-26} \text{ kg} = 1.91 \times 10^3 \text{ kg/s}^2$$

Multiplying the right side of this equation by m/m gives

$$k = 1.91 \times 10^3 \frac{\text{kg m}}{\text{s}^2 \text{ m}} = \underline{\underline{1.91 \times 10^3 \text{ N/m}}}$$

(b) Here $m_1 = 2.33 \times 19^{-26}$ kg   and $\mu = 1.24 \times 10^{-26}$ kg

$$\nu = \frac{1}{2\pi} \sqrt{\frac{1.91 \times 10^3}{1.24 \times 10^{-26}}} = 6.25 \times 10^{13} \text{ s}^{-1}$$

$$\bar{\nu} = 6.25 \times 10^{13} \text{ s}^{-1} / 3.00 \times 10^{10} \text{ cm s}^{-1} = 2083 \text{ cm}^{-1}$$

$$= \underline{\underline{2.08 \times 10^3 \text{ cm}^{-1}}}$$

16-2 (a) We will employ Equation 16-14 to obtain k

$$\bar{\nu} = \frac{1}{2\pi c} \sqrt{\frac{k}{\mu}}$$

where

$$\mu = \frac{m_1 m_2}{m_1 + m_2}$$

$$m_1 = \frac{1.00 \times 10^{-3} \text{ kg/mol H}}{6.02 \times 10^{23} \text{ atom H/mol H}} = 1.66 \times 10^{-27} \text{ kg}$$

$$m_2 = \frac{35.5 \times 10^{-3} \text{ kg/mol Cl}}{6.02 \times 10^{23} \text{ atom Cl/mol Cl}} = 5.90 \times 10^{-26} \text{kg}$$

$$\mu = \frac{1.66 \times 10^{-27} \text{ kg} \times 5.90 \times 10^{-26} \text{ kg}}{1.66 \times 10^{-27} + 5.90 \times 10^{-26} \text{ kg}} = 1.63 \times 10^{-27} \text{ kg}$$

Rearranging Equation 16-14 and substituting gives

$$k = (2\bar{v}\pi c)^2 \mu$$

$$= (2\pi \times 2890 \text{ cm}^{-1} \times 3.00 \times 10^{10} \text{ cm s}^{-1})^2 \times 1.62 \times 10^{-27} \text{ kg}$$

$$= \underline{4.81 \times 10^2 \text{ kg s}^{-2}} = \underline{4.81 \times 10^2 \text{ N/m}}$$

(b) The force constant for HCl and OCl should be the same and

$$m_2 = 2.00 \times 10^{-3}/(6.02 \times 10^{23} = 3.32 \times 10^{-27} \text{ kg}$$

$$\mu = \frac{3.32 \times 10^{-27} \times 5.90 \times 10^{-26}}{3.32 \times 10^{-27} + 5.90 \times 10^{-26}} = 3.14 \times 10^{-17} \text{ kg}$$

$$\bar{v} = \frac{1}{2\pi\, 3.00 \times 10^{10} \text{ cm/s}} \sqrt{\frac{4.79 \times 10^2 \text{ kg s}^{-2}}{3.14 \times 10^{-27} \text{ kg}}} = \underline{2.07 \times 10^3 \text{ cm}^{-1}}$$

16-3 Bonds will be inactive if no change in dipole accompanies the vibration.

(a) Inactive (b) Active (c) Active (d) Active (e) Inactive (f) Active (g) Inactive

16-4 Here we will assume that the force constant for the C – H bond is $5 \times 10^2 \text{ N/m}$ or $5 \text{ kg} \cdot \text{s}^{-2}/\text{m}$ (see page 386) and

$$m_1 = 1.0 \times 10^{-3} \text{ kg mol}^{-1}/6.02 \times 19^{23} \text{ atom/mol}^{-1}$$

$$= 1.66 \times 10^{-27} \text{ kg/atom H}$$

$$m_2 = 12.0 \times 10^{-3}/6.02 \times 10^{23} = 1.99 \times 10^{-26} \text{ kg/atom C}$$

$$\mu = \frac{1.66 \times 10^{-27} \times 1.99 \times 10^{-26}}{1.66 \times 10^{-27} + 1.99 \times 10^{-26}} = 1.53 \times 10^{-27} \text{ kg}$$

Substituting into Equation 16-14

$$\bar{v} = \frac{1}{2\pi c} \sqrt{\frac{k}{\mu}} = 5.3 \times 10^{-10} \frac{\text{s}}{\text{m}} \sqrt{\frac{5 \times 10^2 \text{ kg s}^{-2}}{1.53 \times 10^{-27} \text{ kg}}}$$

$$= 3.03 \times 10^5 \text{m}^{-1} \quad \text{or} \quad \underline{3.0 \times 10^3 \text{ cm}^{-1}}$$

From Table 17-2, range for the C – H band is 2850 to 3300 cm^{-1}.

16-5 $\bar{v} = 1/1.4 \times 10^{-4} \text{ cm} = 7.1 \times 10^3 \text{ cm}^{-1}$

The first overtone occurs as $2\bar{v}$ or $14.2 \times 10^3 \text{cm}^{-1}$

$$\lambda = \frac{1}{1.42 \times 10^3 \text{ cm}^{-1}} = 7.0 \times 10^{-5} \text{ cm} = 0.70 \, \mu\text{m}$$

16-6 Proceeding as in Solution 16-5, we find $\bar{v} = 1.3 \times 10^4 \text{ cm}^{-1}$ and $\lambda = 0.75 \text{ μm}$.

16-7 Sulfur dioxide is a nonlinear triatomic molecule that has $(3 \times 3) - 6 = 3$ vibrational modes including a symmetric and an asymmetric stretching vibration and a scissoring vibration. (See page 383). All three result in absorption peaks.

16-8 The advantages of Fourier transform infrared instruments over dispersives ones include (a) superior signal-to-noise ratios, (2) speed, (e) higher resolution, (4) highly accurate and reproducible frequency information, and (5) freedom from stray radiation effects. The disadvantage of Fourier transform instruments is their higher cost.

16-9 We employ Equation 7-33 (page 189)

$$\Delta\bar{v} = \bar{v}_2 - \bar{v}_1 = \frac{1}{\delta}$$

(a) $\delta = 1/\Delta\bar{v} = 1/0.02 \text{ cm}^{-1} = 50 \text{ cm}$

and length of mirror movement $= 50 \text{ cm} / 2 = \underline{\underline{25 \text{ cm}}}$

(b) In the same way, length $= \underline{\underline{0.25 \text{ cm}}}$

16-10 We write Equation 8-1 (page 199) in the form

$$\frac{N_1}{N_0} = \exp\left(-\frac{E_j}{kT}\right)$$

Here we assume that the degeneracy of the upper and lower states are equal so that $P_j = P_0$.

(a) $E_j = h\nu = hc\bar{v}$

$$= 6.626 \times 10^{-34} \text{ J} \cdot \text{s} \times 3.00 \times 10^{10} \text{cm} \cdot \text{s}^{-1} \times 2885 \text{cm}^{-1} = 5.73 \times 10^{-20} \text{ J}$$

$$\frac{N_1}{N_2} = \exp\left(-\frac{5.73 \times 10^{-20}}{1.38 \times 10^{-23} \times 298}\right) = \underline{\underline{8.9 \times 10^{-7}}}$$

(b) We assume that the energy differences between the ground state and state V = 1 is the same as the difference between states V = 1 and V = 2 or 5.73×10^{-20}. Thus the energy difference between the ground state and the V = 2 state is $2 \times 5.73 \times 10^{-20}$ or 11.46×10^{-20} and

$$\frac{N_2}{N_0} = \exp\left(-\frac{11.46 \times 10^{-20}}{1.38 \times 10^{-23} \times 298}\right) = \underline{\underline{7.9 \times 10^{-13}}}$$

16-11 The white light interferometer is eliminated in some modern instruments because the infrared interferogram also has its maximum at zero retardation, thereby eliminating the need for the white light interferogram.

16-12 The *S/N* ratio for the co-addition process increases in proportion to the square root of the number of individual interferograms that have been added (Equation 5-11, page 108). Thus a 10-fold increase in *S/N* requires a 100-fold increase in the number of interferograms that must be added and collected or $16 \times 100 = 1.6 \times 10^3$.

16-13 According to Equation 7-24 (page 187).

$$f = 2 v_M \bar{v}$$

(a) $f = 2 \times 1.00 \,\text{cm s}^{-1} \times 1700 \,\text{cm}^{-1}$

$\qquad = 3.4 \times 10^3 \,\text{s}^{-1} = \underline{\underline{3.40 \times 10^3 \,\text{Hz}}}$

(b) $\underline{\underline{3.42 \times 10^3 \,\text{Hz}}}$

(c) $\underline{\underline{3.43 \times 10^3 \,\text{Hz}}}$

CHAPTER 17

17-1 (a) The wavenumber of the absorption peak is about 1710 cm^{-1}. An examination of Table 17-2 and Figure 17-5 suggests that this peak arises from the C=O groups in the compound.

(b) Examination of Figure 17-1 reveals that any of the chlorinated solvents as well as cyclohexane could be used. The last is probably preferable from the standpoint of cost and toxicity.

(c) If we assume that the blank has zero absorbance at this wavelength and that the smallest distinguishable signal is three times the standard deviation, the smallest detectable signal will be 0.003. Beer's law takes the form

$$A = abc$$

$$0.40 = ab \times 2.00 \,\text{mg/mL}$$

$$0.003 = ab \times c_{\min}$$

Dividing the second equation by the first permits calculation of the detection limit. Thus,

$$c_{\min} = \frac{0.003}{0.40} \times 2.00 \,\text{mg/mL} = \underline{\underline{1.5 \times 10^{-2} \,\text{mg/mL}}}$$

17-2 The broad band at ~ 3400 cm^{-1} is typical of alcohols. Vinyl alcohol with a formula C_3H_6O is suggested.

The peaks at 2950 cm^{-1} and 1650 cm^{-1} are compatible with this structure.

17-3 The strong peak at 1700 cm⁻¹ suggests that the compound is an aldehyde or ketone. The lack of a peak at 2800 cm⁻¹, however, favors the latter. The empirical formula plus the pattern of four peaks in the 1600 to 1450 cm⁻¹ range is strong evidence for an aromatic structure. The peak 1250 cm⁻¹ suggest an aromatic ketone. Thus, possible structures are

(In fact, the spectrum is for *o*-methyl acetophenone.)

17-4 The strong absorption peak at about 1710 cm⁻¹ suggests the presence of a carbonyl group while the peaks just below 2800 cm⁻¹ indicate that the compound contains an alkane or alkene group. The broad peak at about 3500 cm⁻¹ is probably an OH stretching bond. Thus the compound would appear to be a carboxylic acid. We find, however, no low molecular weight carboxylic acid with a boiling point as low as 50°C. A table of boiling points of aldehydes, on the other hand, reveals the acrolein ($CH_2 = CH - CHO$) has a boiling point of 52°C (it also has a sharp odor). The data are all compatible with this compound providing we assume that the OH bond is a consequence of water in the sample.

17-5 The sharp peak at 2250 cm⁻¹ is characteristic of nitrile or alkyne groups. No evidence for aromatic structure is found in the 1600 to 1450 cm⁻¹ range. Thus, the peaks at about 3000 cm⁻¹ are probably for aliphatic hydrogens. The pair of peaks between 1425 and 1475 cm⁻¹ are compatible with one or more alkane groups. No evidence for amine or amide groups is seen. Thus, it seems likely that the compound is an alkyl nitrile. Propanenitrile ($CH_3CH_2C \equiv N$) boils at 97°C and it seems probable that the unknown is this compound.

17-6 For near-infrared measurements, photoconductor detectors are employed, which are more reproducible in behavior than are the thermal detectors that are required for the mid-infrared region.

17-7 At low transmittance readings, the power of radiation reaching the detector approaches zero and with null type dispersive instruments the exact null position cannot be established accurately. As a consequence overshooting of a transmittance peak can occur, which results in a negative transmittance reading.

17-8 Most infrared transmittances are obtained by comparing the power of the beam after it has passed through the analyte contained in a cell or a null with the power of the unobstructed beam. Reflection and absorption by the cell walls, however, result in attenuation of the beam even in regions when the analyte does not absorb. Thus, the resulting transmittance is less than 100%.

17-9 We will employ Equation 17-2 (page 407). Thus,

$$b = \frac{\Delta N}{2(\bar{v}_1 - \bar{v}_2)}$$

where $\Delta N = 12$ and

$$\bar{\nu}_1 \;=\; \frac{1}{\lambda_1} \;=\; \frac{1}{6.0\,\mu m \times 10^{-4}\,cm/\mu m} \;=\; 1667\ cm^{-1}$$

$$\bar{\nu}_2 \;=\; \frac{1}{1.22 \times 10^{-4}} \;=\; 820\ cm^{-1}$$

$$b \;=\; \frac{12}{2\,(1667 - 820)\ cm^{-1}} \;=\; 7.1 \times 10^{-3}\ cm$$

17-10 $b \;=\; \dfrac{9.5}{2(1480 - 1250)} \;=\; \underline{\underline{0.021\ cm}}$ (see previous solution)

17-11 Between 2700 cm^{-1} and 2000 cm^{-1}, there are 11 minima. Thus,

$$b \;=\; \frac{11}{2(700\ cm^{-1})} \;=\; \underline{\underline{7.9 \times 10^{-3}\ cm}}$$

CHAPTER 18

18-1 Anti-Stokes scattering involves promotion of an electron in the first vibrational state of the electronic ground states to a virtual state that is greater in energy than the virtual state resulting from the promotion of an electron from the lowest vibrational level of the ground state (see Figure 18-2). The number of molecules in the first vibrational level of the ground state increases with temperature increases. Thus the ratio of anti-Stokes to Stokes intensity increases with temperature increases.

18-2 A virtual state is an unquantized electronic energy state that lies between the ground state of a molecule and an excited quantized electronic state.

18-3 Let $\bar{\nu}_{ST}$ and λ_{ST} = wavenumber and wavelength (nm) of Stokes line

$\bar{\nu}_{AST}$ and λ_{AST} = wavenumber and wavelength (nm) of anti-Stokes line

λ = excitation wavelength

$$\bar{\nu}_{ST} \;=\; \bar{\nu}_{source} - \Delta\bar{\nu} \qquad \text{and} \qquad \bar{\nu}_{AST} \;=\; \bar{\nu}_{source} + \Delta\bar{\nu}$$

$$\bar{\nu}_{ST} \;=\; \frac{10^7\ nm/cm}{\lambda\ cm} - \Delta\bar{\nu} \qquad \text{and} \qquad \bar{\nu}_{AST} \;=\; \frac{10^7}{\lambda} + \Delta\bar{\nu}$$

$$\lambda_{ST} \;=\; \frac{10^7}{\bar{\nu}_{ST}} \;=\; \frac{10^7}{10^7/\lambda - \Delta\bar{\nu}} \;=\; \frac{10^7\lambda}{10^7 - \Delta\bar{\nu}\lambda} \;=\; \frac{\lambda}{1 - \Delta\bar{\nu}\lambda \times 10^{-7}}$$

Similarly,

$$\lambda_{AST} = \frac{\lambda}{1 + \Delta\bar{v}\lambda \times 10^{-7}}$$

For $\lambda = 632.8$ and $\Delta\bar{v} = 218$

$$\lambda_{ST} = \frac{632.8}{1 - 218 \times 632.8 \times 10^{-7}} = 641.7 \text{ nm}$$

$$\lambda_{AST} = \frac{632.8}{1 + 218 \times 632.8 \times 10^{-7}} = 624.2 \text{ nm}$$

For	(a)		(b)	
$\Delta\bar{v}$, cm^{-1}	λ, Stokes	λ, Anti-Stokes	λ, Stokes	λ, Anti-Stokes
218	641.7	624.2	493.2	482.9
314	645.6	620.5	495.6	480.6
459	651.7	614.9	499.2	477.3
762	664.9	603.7	506.8	470.5
790	666.1	602.7	507.6	469.9

18-4 (a) The intensity of Raman lines varies directly as the fourth power of the excitation frequency. Thus,

$$I = K' \times v^4 = K/\lambda^4$$

For the argon laser

$$I_{Ar} = K/\lambda_{Ar}^4$$

and $$I_{He/Ne} = K/\lambda_{He/Ne}^4$$

$$\frac{I_{Ar}}{I_{He/Ne}} = \frac{K/(488.0 \text{ mm})^4}{K/(632.8 \text{ mm})^4} = \left(\frac{632.8}{488.0}\right)^4 = 2.83$$

(b) The recorded intensity ratio would almost certainly differ from the ratio computed in part (a) because the efficiency of the photoelectric detector is wavelength dependent.

18-5 The most obvious reason for selecting a He/Ne source would be because either the analyte or some other component in the sample absorbs at the wavelengths available with the Ar$^+$ source, but not at 632.8 nm. A second reason for selecting the He/Ne source is that its energy output is much less than that of most lines of an Ar$^+$ source (typically 50 mW compared with 5 W), and this makes it the preferred source if the compound being studied is photochemically decomposed. Furthermore, the intensity ratio of the Raman line intensities to the background fluorescence intensity often improves at longer wavelengths.

18-6 $\dfrac{N_1}{N_0} = \exp\left(-\dfrac{E_j}{kt}\right)$ (Equation 8 – 1, page 199)

The intensity ratio of the Stokes to the anti-Stokes line (I_{AST}/I_{St}) will be equal to the ratio of the number of reactive species in the ground state N_0 to the number in the first excited state N_1.

(a) $\nu = \bar{\nu}c = 218\ \text{cm}^{-1} \times 3 \times 10^{10}\ \text{cm/s} = 6.54 \times 10^{12}\ \text{s}^{-1}$

     $E_j = h\nu = 6.626 \times 10^{-34}\ \text{J s} \times 6.54 \times 10^{12}\ \text{s}^{-1} = 4.33 \times 10^{-21}\ \text{J}$

At 20°C ≡ 293 K

     $\dfrac{I_{AST}}{I_{ST}} = \dfrac{N_1}{N_0} = \exp\left(-\dfrac{4.33 \times 10^{-21}\ \text{J}}{1.38 \times 10^{-23}\ \text{J K}^{-1} \times 293\ \text{K}}\right) = \underline{\underline{0.342}}$

At 40°C ≡ 313 K

     $\dfrac{I_{AST}}{I_{ST}} = \underline{\underline{0.367}}$

(b) At $\Delta\bar{\nu} = 459$, $E_j = 9.12 \times 10^{-21}\ \text{J}$

     At 20°C, $I_{AST}/I_{ST} = \underline{\underline{0.105}}$

     At 40°C, $I_{AST}/I_{ST} = \underline{\underline{0.121}}$

(c) At $\nu = 790$, $E_j = 1.57 \times 10^{-20}\ \text{J}$

     At 20°C, $I_{AST}/I_{ST} = \underline{\underline{0.0206}}$

     At 40°C, $I_{AST}/I_{ST} = \underline{\underline{0.0264}}$

18-7 (a) $p = \dfrac{I_\perp}{I_\parallel} = \dfrac{0.46}{0.6} = \underline{\underline{0.77}}$

(b) $\dfrac{I_\perp}{I_\parallel} = \dfrac{0.1}{8.4} = \underline{\underline{0.012}}$ $\underline{\underline{\text{polarized}}}$

(c) $\dfrac{I_\perp}{I_\parallel} = \dfrac{0.6}{7.9} = \underline{\underline{0.076}}$ $\underline{\underline{\text{polarized}}}$

(d) $\dfrac{I_\perp}{I_\parallel} = \dfrac{3.2}{4.2} = \underline{\underline{0.76}}$

CHAPTER 19

19-1 In a continuous wave NMR experiment, the intensity of the absorption signal is monitored as the frequency of the source or the field strength of the magnet is scanned. In a Fourier transform NMR experiment, the analyte is subjected to periodic pulses of radio-frequency radiation. After each pulse, the decay of the emitted signal is monitored as a function of time. This free induction decay signal is then converted to a frequency domain signal by a Fourier transformation.

19-2 The advantages of Fourier transform NMR include must greater sensitivity, which results in marked improvements in signal-to-noise ratios and makes possible recording proton spectra on microgram quantities of sample and carbon-13 spectra on samples that contain the isotope in natural abundance concentrations; significant reduction in time required to record spectra; greater frequency reproducibility; and appreciably higher resolution. The main disadvantage of Fourier transform instruments is their cost.

19-3 First, if line width is constant, resolution improves with field strength. Second, sensitivity improves with field strength according to Equation 19-8. Third, as the $\Delta v/J$ ratio increases (page 466), spectral interpretation becomes easier.

19-4 Spin-spin splitting is independent of the magnitude of the magnetic field strength, whereas chemical shifts increase with increases in field strength.

19-5 (a) Magnetic anisotropy is a property of a molecule having magnetic properties that vary with orientation of the molecule.

(b) The screening constant σ is a constant that measures the degree to which circulation of electrons around a nucleus reduce (or sometimes increase) the magnetic field felt by the nucleus. It is defined by the equation

$$\sigma = \frac{B_{appl} - B_0}{B_0}$$

where B_{appl} is the external field and B_0 is the field felt by the nucleus.

(c) The chemical shift parameter measures the shift in parts per million of the peak for a given nucleus from the peak of a reference (usually TMS). It is defined Equations 19-18 and 19-19:

$$\delta = [(v_r - v_s)/v_r] \times 10^6$$

where v_r and v_s are the resonance frequencies of the reference and the sample, respectively.

(d) Continuous wave NMR measurements are performed by measuring the amplitude of the NMR signal as the radio frequency of the source is varied or as the field strength of the magnet is scanned.

(e) The Larmor frequency v_0 is the frequency of precession of a nucleus in an external field. It is given by the relationship

$$\nu_0 = \gamma B_0 / 2\pi$$

where γ is the magnetogyric ratio for the nucleus and B_0 is the magnetic field at the nucleus.

(f) The coupling constant is the spacing in frequency units between the peaks produced by spin-spin splitting.

(g) First-order NMR spectra in which the chemical shift between interacting groups $\Delta\nu$ is large with respect to their coupling constant ($\Delta\nu/J > 10$).

19-6 The number of magnetic energy states is give by $2I + 1$, where I is the spin quantum number. Thus, the number of energy states is $2(5/2) + 1 = 6$, and the magnetic quantum number of each is $+5/2$, $+3/2$, $+1/2$, $-1/2$, $-3/2$, and $-5/2$.

19-7
$$\nu_0 = \frac{\gamma B_0}{2\pi}$$

(a) For ^1H, $\gamma = 2.68 \times 10^8$ (Table 19 – 1)   and

$$\nu_0 = \frac{2.68 \times 10^8 \text{ T}^{-1} \text{ s}^{-1} \times 2.4 \text{ T}}{2\pi} = 1.0 \times 10^8 \text{ Hz} = \underline{\underline{100 \text{ MHz}}}$$

(b) For ^{13}C, $\gamma = 6.73 \times 10^7$ and $\nu_0 = \underline{\underline{2.6 \times 10^7 \text{ Hz}}}$

(c) For ^{19}F, $\gamma = 2.52 \times 10^8$ and $\nu_0 = \underline{\underline{9.6 \times 10^7 \text{ Hz}}}$

(d) For ^{31}P, $\gamma = 1.08 \times 10^8$ and $\nu_0 = \underline{\underline{4.1 \times 10^7 \text{ Hz}}}$

19-8 Spin-spin splitting for $^{13}C/^{13}C$ is not observed in ordinary organic compounds because the probability of two ^{13}C carbons being adjacent to one another is vanishingly small.

19-9 Here, we employ Equation 19-7 (page 448) and write

$$\frac{N_j}{N_0} = \exp\left(-\frac{\gamma h B_0}{2\pi kT}\right)$$

$$= \exp\left(-\frac{6.73 \times 10^7 \text{ T}^{-1} \text{ s}^{-1} \times 6.626 \times 10^{-14} \text{ J s} \times 2.4 \text{ T}}{2\pi \times 1.38 \times 10^{-23} \text{ J K}^{-1} \times 298 \text{ K}}\right)$$

$$= \exp(-4.1 \times 10^{-6}) = \underline{\underline{0.9999959}}$$

19-10 Longitudinal, or spin-lattice, relaxation arises from the complex magnetic fields that are generated by the rotational and vibrational motions of the host of other nuclei making up a sample. At least some of these generated magnetic fields must correspond in frequency and phase with that of the analyte nucleus and can thus convert it from the higher to lower spin state. Transverse, or spin-spin, relaxation, in contrast, is brought about by interaction between neighboring nuclei having identical precession rates but different magnetic quantum states. Here, the nucleus in the lower spin state is excited while the excited nucleus relaxes. No net change in the spin state population occurs but the average lifetime of a particular excited nucleus is shortened.

19-11 The radio-frequency excitation pulse used in FT NMR causes the sample magnetization vector to tip away from the direction of the external magnetic field. Upon termination of the pulse, the same magnetic moment rotates around the external field axis at the Larmor frequency. This motion constitutes a radio-frequency signal that decays to zero as the excited nuclei relax. This decreasing signal is the free induction decay (FID) signal.

19-12 A rotating frame of reference consists of a set of mutually perpendicular coordinates (usually labeled x', y', and z') in which the x' and y' coordinates rotate at a constant rate around the z' coordinate.

19-13 Writing Equation 19-4 (page 448) for the two nuclei gives

$$\Delta E \, (^{13}C) \;=\; \gamma_C h B_0 / 2\pi \;=\; 6.73 \times 10^7 \, h B_0 / 2\pi$$

$$\Delta E \, (^1H) \;=\; \gamma_H h B_0 / 2\pi \;=\; 2.68 \times 10^8 \, h B_0 / 2\pi$$

Dividing the first equation by the second gives

$$\frac{\Delta E \, (^{13}C)}{\Delta E \, (^1H)} \;=\; \underline{0.251}$$

19-14 (a) $\gamma_{^{19}F} \;=\; 2.5181 \times 10^8 \, T^{-1} \, s^{-1}$

$$v_0 \;=\; \frac{\gamma B_0}{2\pi} \;=\; \frac{2.5181 \times 10^8 \, T^{-1} \, s^{-1} \times 5.0 \, T}{2\pi} \;=\; \underline{\underline{200 \, MHz}}$$

(b) $\gamma_{^{31}P} \;=\; 1.0841 \times 10^8 \, T^{-1} \, s^{-1}$

$$v_0 \;=\; \frac{1.0841 \times 10^8 \, T^{-1} \, s^{-1} \times 5.0 \, T}{2\pi} \;=\; \underline{\underline{86 \, MHz}}$$

19-15 In the first printing of the text, the answers to the problems in Chapter 19 beginning with Problem 19-15 on page ANS-17 are misnumbered. The answer to Problem 19-15 should be labeled 19-17, 19-16 should be labeled 19-18, and so on throughout the remaining answers of this chapter.

$$\frac{N_j}{N_0} \;=\; e^{-\Delta E / kT}$$

For the proton in a $v_0 = 220\,\text{MHz}$ instrument

$$v_0 = \frac{\gamma_H B_0}{2\pi} \quad \text{and} \quad B_0 = \frac{2\pi v_0}{\gamma_H}$$

For ^{13}C,

$$\Delta E = \frac{\gamma_C h B_0}{2\pi} = \frac{\gamma_C h}{2\pi} \cdot \frac{2\pi v_0}{\gamma_H} = \frac{\gamma_C}{\gamma_H} \cdot h v_0$$

and

$$\frac{N_j}{N_0} = \exp\left(-\frac{\gamma_c}{\gamma_H} \cdot \frac{h v_0}{kT}\right) = \exp\left(-\frac{0.67283 \times 6.62608 \times 10^{-34}\,J\,s \times 220\,\text{MHz}}{2.6752 \times 1/28066 \times 10^{-23}\,J\,K^{-1} \times 209K}\right)$$

$$= \exp(-8.911947 \times 10^{-6}) = \underline{0.99999109}$$

19-16 According to Equation 19-10 (page 449) the ^1H and ^{31}P spectra should be found in the following frequency ranges

$$v_0\,(^1H) = \frac{\gamma\,(^1H)\,B_0}{2\pi}$$

$$= \frac{2.68 \times 10^8\,T^{-1}\,s^{-1} \times 1.4\,T}{2\pi} = \underline{\underline{59\,\text{MHz}}}$$

Similarly,

$$v_0\,(^{31}P) = \underline{\underline{24\,\text{MHz}}}$$

The lesser frequency at which ^{31}P resonates means that the energy gap for this nucleus is smaller than for the proton. Therefore, the net magnetization vector for ^{31}P will be smaller and the signal per atom for ^{31}P will be lower even though isotopic abundances are approximately the same. This means that the ^1H signal will be much more intense than that due to ^{31}P.

Weak spin-spin coupling means the ^1H signal will be split into a doublet while the ^{31}P signal will be given as the coefficients of the expansion of $(1 + x)^9$.

19-17 According to entries 21 and 23 in Figure 19-17 the chemical shifts in methanol should be ~ 3.6 ppm and ~ 6.0 ppm for the methyl and hydroxyl protons, respectively. In reality both of these are considerably different than their empirical values, but the order is correct, and will therefore be used.

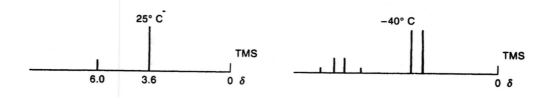

19-18 (a)

¹H spectrum at ~ 130 MHz   ¹⁹F spectrum at ~ 120 MHz

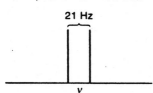

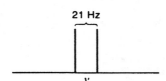

(b)

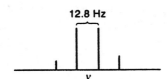

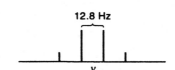

(c)

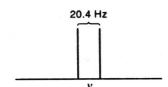

10 peaks with areas proportional to the coefficients in the expansion of $(1 + x)^9$

19-19 The data in Figure 19-32 are used for assigning chemical shifts.

(a)

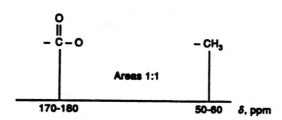

(b)

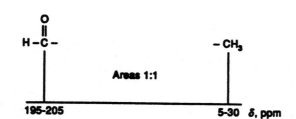

81

(c)

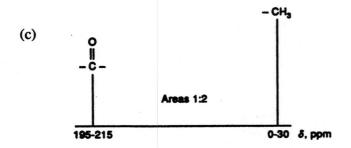

Areas 1:2

195-215   0-30   δ, ppm

19-20 Although it was not mentioned in the text $^{13}C - {}^1H$ coupling constants usually fall in the range of 100 to 200 Hz.

(a)

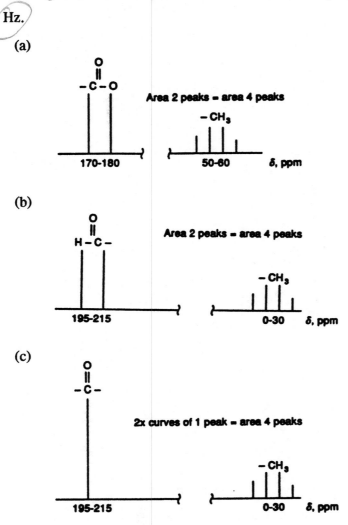

Area 2 peaks = area 4 peaks

– CH₃

170-180   50-60   δ, ppm

(b)

H – C –

Area 2 peaks = area 4 peaks

– CH₃

195-215   0-30   δ, ppm

(c)

– C –

2x curves of 1 peak = area 4 peaks

– CH₃

195-215   0-30   δ, ppm

NOTE: Often $^{13}C - {}^1H$ coupling can extend through a number of bonds but in this problem it was assumed that ^1H would only couple to the ^{13}C to which it is bonded.

19-21 CH_3CH_2COOH

From Table 19-2 and Figure 19-17 we deduce that the carboxylic acid proton should produce a single peak at $\delta = 11$ to 12, the methylene proton four peaks (area ratio = 1:3:3:1 centered about $\delta = 2.2$, and the methyl proton three peaks (area ration 1:2:1) at about $\delta = 1.1$.

19-22

(a) $CH_3\overset{\overset{\displaystyle O}{\|}}{C} - H$

The single proton should produce four peaks (area ratio 1:3:3:1) at $\delta = 9.7$ to 9.8; the methyl proton should yield a doublet at $\delta = 2.2$.

(b) $CH_3\overset{\overset{\displaystyle O}{\|}}{C}OH$

The carboxylic acid proton should produce a singlet peak at $\delta = 11$ to 12, while the three methyl protons should also give a singlet peak at $\delta = 2.2$.

(c) $CH_3CH_2NO_2$

The methylene protons should yield a quartet of peaks (area ratio = 1:3:3:1 centered about $\delta = 4.4$; the methyl protons should give three peaks (area ratio = 1:2:1) centered about $\delta = 1.6$.

19-23   (a) $CH_3 - \overset{\overset{\displaystyle O}{\|}}{C} - CH_3$

Because all of the protons are identical, there should be a single peak at $\delta = 2.1$.

(b) $CH_3 - \overset{\overset{\displaystyle O}{\|}}{C} - CH_2CH_3$

　　　　a　　　　**b**　**c**

The protons on carbon atom **a** will yield a singlet at $\delta = 2.1$. The protons on atom **b** should yield a quartet (1:3:3:1) centered about $\delta = 2.4$ while the proton on atom **c** will give triplet peaks (1:2:1) at 1.1.

(c) $CH_3 - \overset{\overset{\displaystyle O}{\|}}{C} - \overset{\overset{\displaystyle CH_3}{|}}{C}H - CH_3$

The methyl group adjacent to the carbonyl will give a singlet at $\delta = 2.1$. The six methyl protons will yield a doublet (1:1) while the single proton should yield seven peaks centered at $\delta = 2.6$.

19-24   (a) C_6H_{12}

All the protons are equivalent. Thus the compound will yield a single peak at $\delta = 1.2$ to 1.4.

(b) $CH_3OCH_2CH_2OCH_3$

The protons on the two methyl groups should yield a single peak at $\delta = 3.2$. The protons on the other two carbon atoms will also yield a single peak at $\delta = 3.4$. The ratio of peak areas will be 6:4.

(c) $CH_3CH_2OCH_2CH_3$

The two methylene protons should give rise to a quartet at about $\delta = 3.4$. The methyl protons should produce a triplet at $\delta = 1.2$.

19-25 (a) $C_6H_5CH_3$

The five protons on the aromatic ring will yield a single peak at $\delta = 6.5$ to 8. The three methyl protons will give a peak at $\delta = 2.2$.

(b) $C_6H_5CH_2CH_3$

The five protons on the aromatic ring will produce a single peak at $\delta = 6.5$ to 8. The two methylene protons will yield a quartet centered at $\delta = 2.6$. The methyl proton will give a triplet at $\delta = 1.1$.

(c) $(CH_3)_3CH$

The nine methyl protons should appear as a doublet at $\delta = 0.9$. The single proton will appear as ten peaks centered about $\delta = 1.5$.

19-26 The triplet patterns at $\delta = 1.6$ to 7 suggest a methyl group with a brominated methylene groups in the α position. The quartet $\delta = 3.4$ would then arise from the protons on the methylene group. The compound is ethyl bromide.

19-27 The empirical formula and the peak at $\delta = 11$ suggests a carboxylic acid. The triplet at $\delta = 1.1$ would appear to be a methyl group adjacent to a methylene group. The upfield triplet at $\delta = 4.2$ is compatible with –CHBr– group. Thus the compound is

$$\overset{Br}{\underset{|}{CH_3CH_2CHCOOH}}$$

19-28 The strong singlet peak suggests a methyl group adjacent to a carbonyl group. The absence of a peak at $\delta > 9.7$ eliminates the possibility of an aldehyde group and suggests that the compound is a ketone. The four peaks at $\delta = 2.5$ would appear to be from a methylene group adjacent to a methyl group as well as a ketone group. Thus the compound appears to be methyl ethyl ketone.

19-29 The strong singlet at 2.1 and the empirical formula suggests a methyl group adjacent to a –COOR group. The triplet and quartet structure is compatible with an ethylene group. Thus the compound appears to be ethyl acetate.

19-30 The peaks at $\delta = 7$ to 7.5 suggest an aromatic ring as does the empirical formula if this is true the compounds must be isomers having the formula $C_6H_5C_2H_5$ and would be either

(a) C_2H_5

(b) CH_3 — CH_3

The triplet and quartet splitting in Figure 19-45a is compatible with the ethylene group in ethyl benzene. Thus the spectrum in Figure 19-45b must be for one of the dimethylbenzene isomers.

19-31 A notable feature of the NMR spectrum shown in Figure 19-46 is the broad peak at $\delta = 7.2$ corresponding to five protons; a monosubstituted aromatic ring is suggested. The other signal is a sharp singlet at $\delta = 1.3$ with an area of nine protons. The chemical shift of this singlet indicates a saturated methyl group. The methyl groups cannot be attached to any electron withdrawing substituents or it would be shifted further downfield. Since the integrated area corresponds to nine protons, it seems likely that the compound contains three equivalent methyl groups. We now know that this unknown contains the following pieces:

$$CH_3 \qquad CH_3 \qquad CH_3$$

When these are combined with the addition of one carbon, we get *t*-butylbenzene,

A singlet at $\delta = 1.3$ with an area corresponding to nine protons is usually indicative of a *t*-butyl group.

19-32 The set of signals between $\delta = 6.5$ and 8.0 immediately suggests an aromatic ring. It is clear that the ring must be disubstituted and the splitting pattern is indicative of para substitution. A para substituted ring gives this characteristic pattern because the two types of protons,

H_a and H_b, are together to give two doublets. It is also clear that this compound must contain an ethyl group, which causes the triplet at $\delta = 1.3$ and the quartet at $\delta = 4.0$. The chemical shift of the quartet is considerably further downfield than expected for a saturated ethyl group. This shift suggests that the ethyl group must be bonded to a strongly electronegative atom--such as an oxygen. The singlet at $\delta = 2.1$ is probably a methyl group on an electronegative atom. The broad singlet at $\delta = 9.5$ is most likely a proton on an oxygen or nitrogen. The foregoing analysis yields the following parts:

The empirical formula is $C_{10}H_{13}NO_2$ so we still need to account for $C_1O_1N_1$. A carbonyl group would account for the C and O. When these pieces are assembled, several possible structures emerge:

(I)	(II)	(III)

However, the problem states that this unknown is a common painkiller, which indicates that phenacitin (structure III) is the correct answer. In the absence of this information, all three structures given are equally correct interpretations of the NMR spectrum.

19-33 A field frequency lock system is used in NMR instruments in order to overcome the effect of magnetic field fluctuations. In this device, a reference nucleus is continuously irradiated, and its output signal is continuously monitored at its resonance maximum. Changes in intensity of this signal control a feedback circuit, the output of which is fed into coils so as to correct for drift in the magnetic field. The drift correction is applicable to signals for all types of nuclei because the ratio of field strength to resonance frequency is constant and independent of the type of nuclei.

19-35 NMR liquid samples are spun along their longitudinal axis to overcome the effects of small field inhomogeneities. In this way, nuclei experience an averaged environment that produces less band broadening.

19-36 A monochromatic source that is pulsed for τ seconds can be shown to be made up of a band of frequencies having a range of $1/\tau$ Hz (see Figure 6-6, page 122). If a 100 MHz instrument is used, the entire carbon-13 spectrum would require a frequency bandwidth (Δf) of

$$100 \times 10^6 \text{ Hz} \times \frac{200 \text{ Hz}}{10^6 \text{ Hz}} = 2 \times 10^4 \text{ Hz}$$

$$\Delta f = 1/(4\tau) \quad \text{or} \quad \tau = 1/(4\,\Delta f)$$

$$\tau = 1/(4 \times 2 \times 10^4\, s^{-1}) \approx 1.25 \times 10^{-5}\, s \quad (12.5\, \mu s)$$

19-37 Folded spectral lines are obtained when the sine or cosine wave making up the signal is sampled less than twice each cycle for Fourier transformation. The consequence of folding is the appearance of spurious bands at lower frequencies.

19-38 The signal from the detector of an NMR instrument is made up of a radio-frequency oscillator, or carrier, signal and an audio-frequency signal from the excited nucleus superimposed on it. The oscillator signal is then subtracted electronically from the detector signal leaving the audio-frequency NMR signal.

19-39 In quadrature detectors, the incoming NMR signal is split and fed into a pair of identical detectors. In one of the detectors, the signal is frequency modulated by 90 deg before the carrier signal is subtracted from it. The outputs from the two detectors are audio signals, one of which is a cosine signal and the other a sine signal. When these time domain signals are transformed to the frequency domain and added, folded signals subtract out and disappear (see Figure 19-25).

19-40 Broad-band and off-resonance decoupling are techniques for eliminating or reducing spin-spin splitting of carbon-13 NMR lines brought about by protons nuclei. In broad-band decoupling, the sample is irradiated by a band of radio-frequency signals that covers the entire proton spectrum. The result is total elimination or proton splitting of carbon-13 lines giving a very simple spectra. In off-frequency decoupling, the sample is irradiated with radiation that is 1000 to 2000 Hz above the proton spectral region. This treatment leads to a partially decoupled spectrum where all but the largest spin-spin shifts are absent. The resulting spectra provide information about the source of peaks in a carbon-13 spectrum. (See Figure 19-31.)

19-41 The nuclear Overhauser effect involves the enhancement of carbon-13 peak areas brought about by broad-ban proton decoupling. The effect arises from direct magnetic coupling between decoupled protons and neighboring carbon-13 nuclei. This interaction results in an increase in the population of the lower-energy state carbon-13 nuclei. An enhancement of the carbon-13 signal by as much as three results.

19-42 One cause of band broadening in solids is dipolar interactions between carbon-13 and proton nuclei. In liquids, these interactions are averaged to zero by the rapid and random motion of molecules. In solids, dipolar interactions between the two types of nuclei result in splittings of peaks, which vary depending upon the angle between C – H bonds and the external field. In solids a large number of orientations of the bonds exist, and hence a large number of splittings can occur thus producing a broad absorption band made up of closely spaced peaks. This type of broadening can be avoided by irradiating the sample with high-power level proton frequencies. The procedure, called bipolar decoupling, is similar to spin decoupling except that much higher power levels are used.

A second cause of band broadening in solids is chemical shift anisotropy, which is discussed in Section 19B-2. The broadening here results from changes in the chemical shift with orientation of the molecule or part of the molecule with respect to the external magnetic field. This type of broadening in solids is eliminated by magic angle spinning in which the sample is spun at greater than 2 kHz at an angle fo 57.4 deg with respect to the direction of the applied magnetic field.

CHAPTER 20

20-1 In a gaseous ionization, the sample is first volatilized (by heating if necessary) and then transmitted to the ionization area for ion formation. In a desorption source, a probe is used and ionization takes place directly from the condensed form of the sample. The advantage of desorption ionization is that it can be applied to high molecular weight and thermally unstable samples. The advantage of gaseous sources are their simplicity and speed (no need to use probe and wait for probe area to be pumped out).

20-2 The most fragmentation and thus the most complex spectra are encountered with electron impact ionization. Field ionization produces the simplest spectra. Chemical and electron ionization produce greater sensitivities than does field ionization.

20-3 Both field ionization and field desorption ionization are performed at anodes containing numerous sharp tips so that very high electrical fields are realized. In field ionization, the sample is volatilized before ionization, whereas field desorption takes place at an anode that has been coated with the sample. The later requires the use of a sample probe.

20-4 (a) The total kinetic energy acquired by an electron moving between the filament and the target will be eV, where e is the charge on the electron and V is the potential difference. Because SS is approximately half way between the filament and the target the total difference in potential must be 140 V, if the electron is to have 70 eV of energy at SS.

(b) An ion formed at point P will almost certainly collide with a solid part of the exit slit as the result of the repeller-accelerating plate potential.

20-5 (a) For CH_4^+, $m/z = 16$ and

$$16 = \frac{B^2 r^2 e}{2V} = kB^2 = k(0.126\,T)^2 \quad \text{(Equation 20-9, page 515)}$$

Similarly, for $m/z = 250$

$$250 = kB^2$$

Dividing the second equation by the first leads to

$$\frac{250}{16} = \frac{B^2}{(0.126\,T)^2}$$

$$B = 0.498\,T$$

Thus to scan the range of m/z of 16 to 250, the field strength would be scanned from 0.126 to 0.498 T.

(b) Here, Equation 20-9 takes the form

$$16 = \frac{B^2 r^2 e}{2V} = \frac{k'}{V} = \frac{k'}{3.00 \times 10^3}$$

At $m/z = 250$

$$250 = k'/V$$

Dividing the second equation by the first gives

$$\frac{16}{250} = \frac{k'/3.00 \times 10^3}{k'/V} = \frac{V}{3.00 \times 10^3}$$

or

$$V = 16 \times 3.00 \times 10^3 / 250 = 192 \text{ V}$$

Thus, scan from <u>3000</u> to <u>192</u> V.

20-6 Here

$$m = 10{,}000 \frac{g}{mol} \times \frac{1 \text{ mol}}{6.02 \times 10^{23} \text{ ions}} \times \frac{1 \text{ kg}}{10^3 \text{ g}} = 1.66 \times 10^{-23} \frac{kg}{ion}$$

Substituting into Equation 20-9 gives upon rearranging

$$V = \frac{(0.240)^2 (0.127)^2 \, 1.60 \times 10^{-19}}{2 \times 1.66 \times 10^{-23}} = \underline{\underline{4.48 \text{ V}}}$$

20-7 We assume that the initial velocity of the ion along the z direction of the quadrupole is zero. After acceleration the velocity v can be calculated with the aid of Equation 20-4. Thus,

$$zeV = \frac{1}{2} mv^2$$

where m is given by

$$m = 78.0 \frac{g \, C_6H_6^+}{mol} \times \frac{1 \text{ mol}}{6.02 \times 10^{23} \text{ ions}} \times \frac{1 \text{ kg}}{10^3 \text{ g}} = 1.30 \times 10^{-25} \frac{kg}{ion}$$

$$v = \sqrt{\frac{2zeV}{m}} = \sqrt{\frac{2 \times 1.60 \times 10^{-19} \times 5.00}{1.30 \times 10^{-25}}} = 3.51 \times 10^3 \frac{m}{s}$$

$$\text{time} = \frac{15.0 \text{ cm} \times 10^{-2} \text{ m/cm}}{3.51 \times 10^3 \text{ m/s}} = \underline{\underline{4.27 \times 10^{-5} \text{ s}}} \text{ or } \underline{\underline{42.7 \text{ μs}}}$$

20-8 The presence of a negative dc potential in the yz plane causes positive ions to move toward the rods where they are annihilated. In the presence of an added ac potential, this movement is inhibited during the positive half of the cycle with the lighter ions being more affected than the heavier ions. Thus the yz plane acts as a low-pass filter removing heavier ions (see Figure 11-6b, page 259).

20-9 The resolution of a single focusing mass spectrometer is limited by the initial kinetic energy spread of the sample molecules. This spread is minimized in a double focusing instrument by accelerating the sample ions through an electrostatic analyzer, which limits the range of kinetic energies of ions being introduced into the magnetic analyzer. Significantly narrow peaks result.

20-10 Resolution = $m/\Delta m$ (Equation 20-3)

(a) $m/\Delta m$ = $28.0/(28.0187 - 28.0061)$ = $\underline{2.22 \times 10^3}$

(b) $m/\Delta m$ = $28.0/(28.0313 - 27.9949)$ = $\underline{769}$

(c) $m/\Delta m$ — $85.1/(85.0653 - 85.0641)$ = $\underline{7.09 \times 10^4}$

(d) $m/\Delta m$ = $115.9/(232.03800/2) - 115.90219$ = $\underline{992}$

20-11 (a) In Table 20-3 (page 505), we find that for every 100 ^{79}Br atoms there are 98 ^{81}Br atoms. Because the compound in question has two atoms of bromine

$$(M + 2)^+/M^+ = 2 \times 98/100 = \underline{1.96}$$

and

$$(M + 4)^+/M^+ = (98/100)^2 = \underline{0.96}$$

(b) Table 20-3 reveals that for every 100 ^{35}Cl atoms, there are 32.5 ^{37}Cl atoms. Thus,

$$(M + 1)^+/M^+ = (1 \times 98/100) + (1 \times 32.5/100) = \underline{1.30}$$

$$(M + 4)^+/M^+ = (1 \times 98/100)(1 \times 32.5/100) = \underline{0.32}$$

(c) $(M + 2)^+/M^+$ = $2 \times 32.5/100$ = 0.65

$(M + 4)^+/M^+$ = $(32.5/100)^2$ = $\underline{0.106}$

20-12 (a)

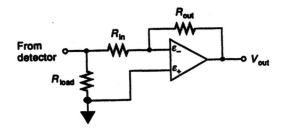

R_{in} should be at least 100 times R_{load}. Setting $R_{out}/R_{in} = 100$ will provide the desired voltage gain. If the previous conditions can not be satisfied it will be necessary to build a voltage follower with gain or a two op amp circuit which uses a voltage follower by a multiplier (see below).

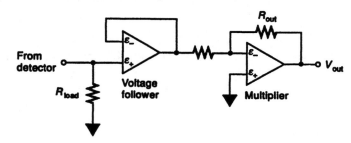

(b)

A current to voltage converter with gain could be used to produce the same V_{out}, but the two op amp circuit better illustrates the processes.

20-13 (a) Because all conditions, except accelerating voltage are constant, Equation 20-9 can be abbreviated to $(m/z)_s = K/V_s$, where K is a constant. Therefore, we can write

$$(m/z)_s = K/V_s \quad \text{and} \quad (m/z)_u = K/V_u$$

The subscripts designate standard (s) and unknown (u). Dividing one of these equations by the other gives the desired relationship.

$$\frac{(m/z)_s}{(m/z)_u} = \frac{K/V_s}{K/V_u} = \frac{V_u}{V_s}$$

(b) $\dfrac{69.00}{(m/z)_u} = \underline{0.965035}$

$(m/z)_u = \underline{71.50}$

(c) The approximately half-integral (m/z) value suggests that the ion being studied in part (b) was doubly charged. This conclusion is in agreement with the fact that the molecular weight of the unknown is 143. The second conclusion is that the unknown must contain an odd number of nitrogen atoms (Nitrogen rule).

20-14 The difference in mass between ^{12}C and ^{13}C is 1.00335. Therefore, making the assumption that $(P + 1)^+$ is due only to ^{13}C means

$$\text{mass } (P + 1) = \text{mass } (P) + 1.00335$$

In Problem 20-13 the following relationship was derived

$$\frac{(m/z)_s}{(m/z)_u} = \frac{V_u}{V_s}$$

Taking into account the fact that only singly charged ions were specified, and rewriting this equation with P representing the standard (s) and $(P + 1)$ representing the unknown (u), the following result is obtained

$$\frac{m\,(P)}{m\,(P+1)} = \frac{m\,(P)}{m\,(P) + 1.00335} = \frac{V\,(P+1)}{V\,(P)}$$

(b) Substituting the voltage ratio into the last equation allows $m\,(P)$ to be calculated.

$$\frac{m\,(P)}{m\,(P) + 1.00335} = \frac{V\,(P+1)}{V\,(P)} = 0.987753$$

$$m\,(P) = \underline{80.92}$$

20-15 (1) Ions produced in the spark have a very wide range of energy. Inserting a slit between the electrostatic sector and the magnetic sector is an excellent means of restricting the energy spread of the ions entering the magnetic sector. The presence of the electrostatic sector means that the ions entering the magnetic sector will be both energy and direction focused at the detector. (2) Certain pairs of ions have very similar mass-to-charge ratios that can only be distinguished with a high-resolution instrument.

20-16 $m = 131$ due to $^{35}Cl_3CCH_2^+$, $m = 133$ due to $^{37}Cl^{35}Cl_2CCH_2^+$,

$m = 135$ due to $^{37}Cl_2^{35}ClCCH_2^+$, $m = 117$ due to $^{35}Cl_3C^+$,

$m = 119$ due to $^{37}Cl^{35}Cl_2C^+$, $m = 121$ due to $^{37}Cl_2^{35}ClC^+$

20-17 $m = 84$ due to $^{35}Cl_2^{12}C^+$, $m = 85$ due to $^{35}Cl_2^{13}CH_2^+$,

$m = 86$ due to $^{37}Cl^{35}Cl^{12}CH_2^+$, $m = 87$ due to $^{37}Cl^{35}Cl^{13}CH_2^+$,

$m = 88$ due to $^{37}Cl_2^{12}CH_2^+$

CHAPTER 21

21-1 An M electron is ejected by X-radiation or by a beam of electrons. An N electron then descends to the M orbital while ejecting a second N electron as an Auger electron.

21-2 Auger and ESCA peaks can be distinguished by comparing spectra obtained with two different sources (such as an Al and Mg tube). Auger peaks are unaffected by the change in source whereas ESCA peaks are displaced by the change.

21-3 The ESCA binding energy is the minimum energy required to remove an inner electron from its orbital to a region where it no longer feels the nuclear charge. The absorption edge results from this same transition. Thus, in principle it is possible to observe chemical shifts by either type of measurement.

21-4 (a) $E_b = h\nu - E_k - w$ (Equation 21 − 2, page 539)

To obtain $h\nu$ in electron volts

$$h\nu = \frac{hc}{\lambda}$$

$$= \frac{6.6256 \times 10^{-34} \text{ J} \cdot \text{s} \times 2.9979 \times 10^{10} \text{ cm/s}}{9.890 \text{ Å} \times 10^{-8} \text{ cm/Å}} \times 6.2418 \times 10^{18} \frac{\text{eV}}{\text{J}} = 1253.6 \text{ eV}$$

$$E_b = 1253.6 - 1073.5 - 14.7 = \underline{165.4 \text{ eV}}$$

(b) From Figure 21-6, E_b for SO_3^{2-} = 165.4. Thus, SO_3^{2-} seems likely.

(c) As in part (a),

$$h\nu = hc/\lambda = 1.2398 \times 10^{-4}/8.3393 \times 10^{-8} = 1486.7 \text{ eV}$$

$$E_k = 1486.7 - 165.4 - 14.7 = \underline{1306.6 \text{ eV}}$$

(d) Kinetic energy of an Auger electron is independent of source energy. Thus, $\underline{1073.5 \text{ eV}}$.

21-5 (a) $E_b = h\nu - E_k - w = h\nu - 1052.5 - 27.8$ (Equation 21 − 2)

From Solution 21-4c, $h\nu = 1486.7 \text{ eV}$

$$E_b = 1486.7 - 1052.6 - 27.8 = \underline{406.3 \text{ eV}}$$

(b) $E_k = h\nu - 406.4 - 27.8$

From Solution 21-4a, $h\nu = 1253.6 \text{ eV}$

$$E_k = 1253.6 - 406.3 - 27.8 = \underline{819.5 \text{ eV}}$$

(c) By obtaining the peak with sources of differing energy (such as Al and Mg X-ray tubes). Auger peaks would not have different kinetic energies with the two sources.

(d) From Table 21-2, it is seen that N $(1s)$ peak for NO_3^- is shifted by +8.0 eV against the reference while that for NO_2^- is shifted 5.1 eV. Thus the binding energy for NO_2^- should be

$$E_b = 406.3 - (8.0 - 5.1) = \underline{\underline{403.4 \text{ eV}}}$$

21-6 According to Equation 21-7 (page 550), the magnification M is given by $M = W/w$, where W is the width of the CRT display and w is the width of a scan across the sample.

(a)
$$\text{scan width} = \frac{20 \text{ cm}}{100} = \underline{\underline{0.20 \text{ cm}}}$$

(b)
$$\text{scan width} = \frac{20 \text{ cm}}{10^5} \times \frac{10^4 \text{ μm}}{\text{cm}} = \underline{\underline{2 \text{ μm}}}$$

21-7 In elastic scattering of electrons, the electrons interact with a solid in such a way that their direction is altered but no energy is lost in the process. In inelastic scattering, the part of the energy of the electron is lost during the scattering process.

21-8 (a) The two types of scanning probe microscopes are the scanning tunneling microscope (STM) and the atomic force microscope (AFM).

(b) In the STM, The surface being studied is scanned with a sharp metallic tip whose position above the surface is controlled by a tunneling current between the tip and the surface. In the ATM the surface is scanned by a fine stylus is mounted on a very force-sensitive cantilever whose vertical position is sensed optically with a laser beam. In contrast to the STM the sensor comes in contact with the sample surface.

(c) The advantage of the STM is that the sensing tip never makes physical contact with the sample surface. The primary advantage of the AFM is that it does not require that the sample be a conductor of electricity.

(d) The main disadvantage of the STM that it requires that the surface being examined be electrical conducting. The chief disadvantage of the AFM is that the stylus tip comes in physical contact with the surface, which may alter the characteristics of the sample.

21-9 Raster scanning is a process in which a surface is studied with a beam of radiation that is moved systematically across a surface in the x direction making observations at regular intervals during the scan. The beam is then returned to its starting position and then moved a small amount in the y direction. The scan in the x direction is then repeated. These scans are then repeated enough time so a desired surface area has been observed.

CHAPTER 22

22-1 (a)
$$E = 0.799 - \frac{0.0592}{1} \log \frac{1}{[Ag^+]} = 0.799 - 0.0592 \log \frac{1}{0.0152}$$

$$= 0.799 - 0.108 = \underline{\underline{0.691 \text{ V}}}$$

(b)
$$E = 0.771 - 0.0592 \log \frac{0.200}{2.35 \times 10^{-4}} = 0.771 - 0.173 = \underline{\underline{0.598 \text{ V}}}$$

(c) $E = 0.073 - 0.0592 \log 0.100 = \underline{\underline{0.132 \text{ V}}}$

22-2 (a)
$$E = 0.000 - \frac{0.0592}{2} \log \frac{p_{H_2}}{[H^+]^2} = 0.000 - \frac{0.0592}{2} \log \frac{0.950}{(3.50)^2} = \underline{\underline{0.033 \text{ V}}}$$

(b)
$$E = 1.178 - \frac{0.0592}{5} \log \frac{(5 \times 10^{-4})^{1/2}}{(0.235)(2 \times 10^{-3})^6} = \underline{\underline{0.998 \text{ V}}}$$

(c)
$$E = 0.446 - \frac{0.0592}{2} \log 0.0250 = 0.446 + 0.047 = \underline{\underline{0.493 \text{ V}}}$$

22-3 $2H^+ + 2e^- \rightleftarrows H_2 \qquad E^0 = 0.000 \text{ V}$

(a) (1) $E = 0.000 - (0.0592/2) \log [1.00/(0.01)^2] = \underline{\underline{-0.118 \text{ V}}}$

(2) $\text{ionic strength} = \mu = \frac{1}{2}[0.01(1)^2 + 0.05(1)^2 + 0.04(1)^2] = 0.05$

(Equation a2-2, Appendix2)

From Table a2-1

$$\gamma_{H^+} = 0.864 \quad \text{and} \quad a_{H^+} = 0.86 \times 0.01 = 8.6 \times 10^{-3}$$

$$E = 0.00 - (0.0592/2) \log[1.00/(8.6 \times 10^{-3})^2] = \underline{\underline{-0.122 \text{ V}}}$$

(b) $Fe^{3+} + e^- \rightleftarrows Fe^{2+} \qquad E^0 = 0.771 \text{ V}$

(1) $E = 0.771 - 0.0592 \log (0.0111/0.0111) = \underline{\underline{0.771 \text{ V}}}$

(2) $\mu = \frac{1}{2}[0.0111(2)^3 + 0.0111(3)^2 + 2 \times 0.0111(1)^2 + 3 \times 0.0111(1)^2] = 0.100$

From Table a2-1

$$\gamma_{Fe^{2+}} = 0.40 \quad \text{and} \quad a_{Fe^{2+}} = 0.40 \times 0.0111 = 0.00444$$

$$\gamma_{Fe^{3+}} = 0.18 \quad \text{and} \quad a_{Fe^{3+}} = 0.18 \times 0.01111 = 0.00200$$

$$E = 0.771 - 0.0592 \log 0.00444/0.00200 = \underline{\underline{0.751 \text{ V}}}$$

22-4 $Sn^{4+} + 2e^- \underset{\leftarrow}{\rightarrow} Sn^{2+} \quad E^0 = 0.154 \text{ V}$

(a) (1) $E = 0.154 - (0.0592/2) \log [2.00 \times 10^{-5}/(1.00 \times 10^{-5})] = \underline{\underline{0.145 \text{ V}}}$

(2) Equation a2-2 takes the form,

$$\mu = \frac{1}{2} [2.00 \times 10^{-5}(2)^2 + 1.00 \times 10^{-5}(4)^2 + 8.00 \times 10^{-5}(1)^2] = 1.6 \times 10^{-4}$$

From Equation a2-3,

$$-\log \gamma_{Sn^{2+}} = \frac{0.509(2)^2 \sqrt{1.6 \times 10^{-4}}}{1 + 0.328 \times 6 \sqrt{1.6 \times 10^{-4}}} = 0.0251$$

$$\gamma_{Sn^{2+}} = 0.944$$

$$a_{Sn^{2+}} = \gamma_{Sn^{2+}} [Sn^{2+}] = 2.00 \times 10^{-5} \times 0.944 = 1.89 \times 10^{-5}$$

$$-\log \gamma_{Sn^{4+}} = \frac{0.509(4)^2 \sqrt{1.6 \times 10^{-4}}}{1 + 0.328 \times 11 \sqrt{1.6 \times 10^{-4}}} = -0.0983$$

$$\gamma_{Sn^{4+}} = 0.797$$

$$a_{Sn^{4+}} = \gamma_{Sn^{4+}} [Sn^{4+}] = 7.97 \times 10^{-6}$$

$$E = 0.154 - (0.0592/2) \log [1.89 \times 10^{-5}/(7.97 \times 10^{-6})] = \underline{\underline{0.143 \text{ V}}}$$

(b) (1) As in Solution 22-4a, $E = \underline{\underline{0.145 \text{ V}}}$

(2) Here the contribution of the tin species to μ is negligible

$$\mu \approx \frac{1}{2} [0.05 \times (1)^2 + 0.05 \times (1)^2] = 0.0500 \quad \text{(Equation a2-2)}$$

From Table a2-1,

$$\gamma_{Sn^{2+}} = 0.48 \quad \text{and} \quad a_{Sn^{2+}} = 0.48 \times 2.00 \times 10^{-5} = 9.60 \times 10^{-6}$$

$$\gamma_{Sn^{4+}} = 0.10 \quad \text{and} \quad a_{Sn^{4+}} = 0.10 \times 1.00 \times 10^{-5} = 1.0 \times 10^{-6}$$

$$E = 0.154 - (0.0592/2) \log [9.60 \times 10^{-6}/(1.0 \times 10^{-4})] = \underline{\underline{0.125 \text{ V}}}$$

22-5 (a) $E = -0.151 - 0.0592 \log 0.0200 = \underline{\underline{-0.050 \text{ V}}}$

(b) $E = -0.31 - 0.0592 \log \dfrac{(0.0060)^2}{0.0400} = -0.31 + 0.180 = \underline{\underline{-0.13 \text{ V}}}$

(c) mmol $Br^- = 25.0 \times 0.0400 = 1.00$

mmol $Ag^+ = 20.0 \times 0.200 = 4.00$

$[Ag^+] = \dfrac{3.00}{45.00} = 0.0667$

$E = 0.799 - 0.0592 \log \dfrac{1}{0.0667} = \underline{\underline{0.729 \text{ V}}}$

(d) mmol $Br^- = 20.0 \times 0.200 = 4.00$

mmol $Ag^+ = 25.0 \times 0.0400 = 1.00$

$[Br^-] = \dfrac{3.00}{45.0} = 0.0667$

$E = 0.073 - 0.0592 \log 0.0667 = \underline{\underline{0.143 \text{ V}}}$

22-6 (a) $E = 1.33 - \dfrac{0.0592}{6} \log \dfrac{(1.00 \times 10^{-2})^2}{(5.00 \times 10^{-3})(0.200)^{14}} = 1.33 - 0.080$

$= \underline{\underline{1.25 \text{ V}}}$

(b) $E = 0.334 - \dfrac{0.0592}{2} \log \dfrac{0.200}{0.100 \times (0.600)^4} = 0.334 - 0.035$

$= \underline{\underline{0.299 \text{ V}}}$

22-7 (a) $E_{cathode} = -0.126 - \dfrac{0.0592}{2} \log \dfrac{1}{6.5 \times 10^{-2}} = -0.161$

$E_{anode} = -0.408 - 0.0592 \log \dfrac{1.00 \times 10^{-3}}{2.00 \times 10^{-4}} = -0.449$

$E_{cell} = -0.161 - (-0.449) = \underline{\underline{0.288 \text{ V}}} \quad \text{galvanic}$

(b) $E_{cathode} = 0.359 - 0.0592 \log \dfrac{2.00 \times 10^{-2}}{6.00 \times 10^{-3}(3.00 \times 10^{-2})^2} = 0.148$

$$E_{anode} = 0.788 - \frac{0.0592}{2} \log \frac{1}{4.00 \times 10^{-2}} = 0.747$$

$$E_{cell} = 0.148 - 0.747 = \underline{-0.599 \text{ V} \quad \text{electrolytic}}$$

(c)
$$E_{cathode} = 0.154 - \frac{0.0592}{2} \log \frac{3.5 \times 10^{-2}}{1.50 \times 10^{-4}} = 0.084$$

$$E_{anode} = 0.771 - 0.0592 \log \frac{6.00 \times 10^{-5}}{2.00 \times 10^{-2}} = 0.920$$

$$E_{cell} = 0.084 - 0.920 = \underline{-0.836 \quad \text{electrolytic}}$$

22-8 (a) $E_{cathode} = -0.151 - 0.0592 \log 0.100 = -0.092$

$$E_{anode} = 0.320 - \frac{0.0592}{3} \log \frac{1}{0.0400 \, (0.200)^2} = 0.265$$

$$E_{cell} = -0.092 - 0.265 = \underline{-0.357 \text{ V} \quad \text{electrolytic}}$$

(b)
$$E_{cathode} = 0.36 - 0.0592 \log \frac{4.50 \times 10^{-2}}{7.00 \times 10^{-2}} = 0.371$$

$$E_{anode} = -0.763 - \frac{0.0592}{2} \log \frac{1}{7.50 \times 10^{-4}} = -0.855$$

$$E_{cell} = 0.371 - (-0.855) = \underline{1.23 \text{ V} \quad \text{galvanic}}$$

(c) $E_{cathode} = 0.222 - 0.0592 \log 4.50 \times 10^{-4} = 0.420$

$$E_{anode} = 0.000 - \frac{0.0592}{2} \log \frac{0.100}{(4.50 \times 10^{-4})^2} = -0.169$$

$$E_{cell} = 0.420 - (-0.169) = \underline{0.589 \text{ V} \quad \text{galvanic}}$$

22-9 $Ni^{2+} + 2e^- \rightleftarrows Ni(s) \qquad E^0 = -0.250$

$$E = -0.250 - \frac{0.0592}{2} \log \frac{1}{[Ni^{2+}]}$$

$$K_f = \frac{[Ni(CN)_4^{2-}]}{[Ni^{2+}][CN^-]^4}$$

$$E = -0.250 - \frac{0.0592}{2} \log \frac{K_f [CN^-]^4}{Ni(CN^{2-})_4}$$

When $[CN^-]^4 / [NiCN_4^{2-}] = 1.00$

$$E = E^0 = -0.250 - \frac{0.0592}{2} \log K_f$$

$$E^0 = -0.250 - \frac{0.0592}{2} \log 1.0 \times 10^{22} = \underline{\underline{-0.90 \text{ V}}}$$

22-10 $Pb^{2+} + 2e^- \rightleftarrows Pb(s) \qquad E^0 = -0.126 \text{ V}$

$$[Pb^{2+}][I^-]^2 = 7.1 \times 10^{-9} = K_{sp}$$

$$E = -0.126 - \frac{0.0592}{2} \log \frac{1}{[Pb^{2+}]} = -0.126 - \frac{0.0592}{2} \log \frac{[I-]^2}{K_{sp}}$$

When $[I^-] = 1.00, \quad E = E^0$

$$E^0 = -0.126 - \frac{0.0592}{2} \log \frac{(1.00)^2}{7.1 \times 10^{-9}} = \underline{\underline{-0.367 \text{ V}}}$$

22-11 Proceeding as in Solution 22-10, we obtain

$$E^0 = \underline{\underline{-0.037 \text{ V}}}$$

22-12 Proceeding as in Solution 22-9, we find

$$E^0 = \underline{\underline{-1.92 \text{ V}}}$$

22-13
$$E = -0.336 - 0.052 \log \frac{1}{[Tl^+]} = -0.336 - 0.0592 \log \frac{[Cl^-]}{K_{sp}}$$

When $[Cl^-] = 1.00, \quad E = E^0_{TlCl} = -0.557$

$$-0.557 = -0.336 - 0.0592 \log \frac{1.00}{K_{sp}}$$

$$-0.221 = -0.0592 \log \frac{1}{K_{sp}}$$

$$\log \frac{1}{K_{sp}} = \frac{-0.221}{-0.0592} = 3.733$$

$$\log K_{sp} = -3.733$$

$$\underline{\underline{K_{sp} = 1.85 \times 10^{-4}}}$$

22-14 Proceeding as Solution 22-13, we obtain

$$\underline{\underline{K_{sp} = 1.0 \times 10^{-15}}}$$

22-15 $E_{cathode} = 0.073 - 0.0592 \log 0.150 = 0.122$

$$E_{anode} = -0.256 - 0.0592 \log \frac{0.165}{1.0 \times 10^{-5}} = -0.506$$

$$E_{cathode} - E_{anode} = 0.122 - (-0.506) = 0.628 \text{ V}$$

$$E_{cell} = 0.627 - 0.0750 \times 6.74 = \underline{\underline{0.123 \text{ V}}}$$

22-16 $E_{cathode} = 0.337 - 0.0592 \log \frac{1}{5.0 \times 10^{-2}} = 0.298$

$$E_{anode} = 1.00 - 0.0592 \log \frac{7.15 \times 10^{-2}}{1.04 \times 10^{-4} (2.75 \times 10^{-3})^2} = 0.529$$

$$E_{cathode} - E_{anode} = 0.298 - 0.529 = 0.230 \text{ V}$$

$$E_{cathode} - E_{anode} - IR = -0.230 - 0.0300 \times 2.24 = \underline{\underline{-0.298 \text{ V}}}$$

22-17 Proceeding as in Solution 22-16, we obtain

$$E_{cell} = 0.693 - 0.293 - 0.043 = \underline{\underline{0.357 \text{ V}}}$$

CHAPTER 23

23-1 Potentiometric titrations are widely applicable and do not require an indicator. They are inherently more accurate than titrations with an indicator. Furthermore, they can be used for titrations of colored solutions or turbid solutions. They also permit the detection of unsuspected species.

Generally, potentiometric titrations require more time than a titration with a colored indicator. Furthermore, the equipment required is more expensive than that for an indicator titration.

23-2 The source of alkaline errors in pH measurements with a glass electrode arises from the exchange of singly charged ions, such as sodium or potassium ions in the surface of the glass membrane with the protons from the water. The potential of the system then responds to the alkali ion activity as well as the hydrogen ion activity.

23-3

Temperature Coefficients for Reference Electrodes, V/°C				
0.1 M Calomel	3.5 M Calomel	Sat'd Calomel	3.5 M Ag/AgCl	Sat'd Ag/Cl
-9×10^{-5}	-4.0×10^{-4}	-6.8×10^{-4}	-7.5×10^{-4}	1.0×10^{-3}

23-4 Hydration of the surface of the glass takes place in which singly charged metal ions in the glass are exchanged with protons of the water.

23-5 An electrode of the second kin is a metal electrode whose potential depends upon the activity of an anion that forms a precipitate with the electrode metallic ion. An electrode of the third kind is a metallic electrode whose potential depends upon the activity of another kind of cation. An example is a mercury electrode that responds to the calcium ion activity of a solution that contains a fixed and small concentration of the EDTA complex of mercury(II).

23-6 For methyl amine, we may write

$$CH_3NH_2 + H_2O \ \rightleftharpoons \ CH_3NH_3^+ + OH^-$$

$$\frac{[CH_3NH_3^+][OH^-]}{[CH_3NH_3^+]} = K_b$$

at the midpoint in the titration of CH_3NH_2 with a strong acid

$$[CH_3NH_3^+] \approx [CH_3NH_2] \quad \text{and} \quad K_b = [OH^-] = \frac{K_w}{[H^+]}$$

$$\frac{1}{[H^+]} = \frac{K_b}{K_w}$$

$$\log \frac{1}{[H^+]} = pH = \log \frac{K_b}{K_w}$$

Thus by measuring the pH at the midpoint in the titration, K_b can be determined by this relationship.

23-7 (a) The boundary potential arises from a difference in potential between the two membrane surfaces arising from the difference in activity of the analyte ion in the solution on either side of the membrane.

(b) The junction potential arises at the two interfaces of the salt bridge that separates the bridge from the analyte solution and the outer reference electrode solution.

(c) The potential of a solid-state fluoride ion electrode arises from the different degree of dissociation of the LaF$_3$ membrane on either side of the membrane. That is, upon the two equilibria

$$\underset{\text{solid}}{LaF_3(s)} \;\rightleftarrows\; \underset{\text{solid}}{LaF_2^+} + \underset{\substack{\text{reference}\\\text{solution}}}{F^-} \qquad \text{inner surface}$$

$$\underset{\text{solid}}{LaF_3(s)} \;\rightleftarrows\; \underset{\text{solid}}{LaF_2^+} + \underset{\substack{\text{analyte}\\\text{solution}}}{F^-} \qquad \text{outer surface}$$

23-8 (a)
$$E_{cathode} = 0.771 - 0.0592 \log \frac{0.0222}{0.0150} = 0.761$$

$$E_{anode} = E_{SCE} = 0.244 \text{ V}$$

$$E_{cell} = E_{cathode} - E_{anode} = 0.761 - 0.244 = 0.517 \text{ V}$$

(b)
$$E_{cathode} = -0.763 - \frac{0.0592}{2} \log \frac{1}{0.00165} = -0.845$$

$$E_{anode} = 0.244$$

$$E_{cell} = -0.845 - 0.244 = -1.089 \text{ V}$$

(c)
$$E_{cathode} = -0.369 - 0.0592 \log \frac{0.0350}{0.0110} = -0.399$$

$$E_{anode} = 0.199 \text{ V}$$

$$E_{cell} = -0.399 - 0.199 = -0.598$$

(d)
$$E_{cathode} = 0.536 - \frac{0.0592}{2} \log \frac{(0.00313)^3}{(0.00562)} = 0.692$$

$$E_{anode} = 0.199$$

$$E_{cell} = 0.692 - 0.199 = 0.493 \text{ V}$$

23-9 (a) $Cu^+ + e^- \;\rightleftarrows\; Cu(s) \qquad E^0 = 0.521$

$$E = 0.521 - 0.0592 \log \frac{1}{[Cu^+]} = 0.521 - 0.0592 \log \frac{[Br^-]}{K_{sp}}$$

When $[Br^-] = 1.00$, $E = E^0_{CuBr}$

$$E = E^0_{CuBr} = 0.521 - 0.0592 \log \frac{1.00}{5.2 \times 10^{-9}}$$

$$E^0_{CuBr} = \underline{0.031 \text{ V}}$$

(b) SCE||CuBr(*sat'd*),Br⁻ (*x*M)|Cu

(c) $E_{cell} = E_{cathode} - E_{anode} = 0.031 - 0.0592 \log [Br^-] - E_{SCE}$

$$= 0.031 + 0.0592 \, pBr - 0.244$$

$$pBr = (E_{cell} - 0.031 + 0.244)/(0.0592) = (E_{cell} + 0.213)/0.0592$$

(d) $pBr = (-0.071 + 0.213)/(0.0592) = \underline{2.40}$

23-10 **(a)** $Ag_3AsO_4(s) = 3Ag^+ + AsO_4^{3-}$ $K_{sp} = [Ag^+]^3 [AsO_4^{3-}] = 1.2 \times 10^{-22}$

For $Ag^+ + e^- \rightleftharpoons Ag(s)$, $E^0 = 0.799$

$$E = 0.799 - 0.0592 \log \frac{1}{Ag^+} = 0.799 - \frac{0.0592}{3} \log \frac{1}{[Ag^+]^3}$$

$$E = 0.799 - \frac{0.0592}{3} \log \frac{[AsO_4^{3-}]}{K_{sp}}$$

When $[AsO_4^{3-}] = 1.00$, $E = E^0_{Ag_3AsO_4}$

$$E^0_{Ag_3AsO_4} = 0.799 - \frac{0.0592}{3} \log \frac{1.00}{1.2 \times 10^{-22}} = \underline{0.366 \text{ V}}$$

(b) SCE||Ag₂AsO₄(*sat'd*),AsO₄³⁻(*x*M)|Ag

(c) $E_{cell} = 0.366 - \frac{0.0592}{3} \log [AsO_4^{3-}] - E_{SCE}$

$$= 0.366 + \frac{0.0592}{3} pAsO_4 - 0.244 = 0.122 + \frac{0.0592}{3} pASO_4$$

$$pAsO_4 = \frac{(E_{cell} - 0.122) \times 3}{0.0592}$$

(d) $pAsO_4 = \frac{(0.312 - 0.122) \, 3}{0.0592} = \underline{9.62}$

23-11 $Ag_2CrO_4(s) + 2e^- = 2Ag(s) + CrO_4^{2-}$ $E^0 = 0.446 \text{ V}$

$$E_{cell} = E_{SCE} - \left(0.446 - \frac{0.0592}{2} \log [CrO_4^{2-}] \right)$$

$$-0.402 = 0.244 - 0.446 + \frac{0.0592}{2} \log [CrO_4^{2-}] = -0.202 - \frac{0.0592}{2} pCrO_4$$

$$pCrO_4 = \frac{(-0.202 + 0.402) 2}{0.0592} = \underline{\underline{6.76}}$$

23-12 $Hg_2SO_4(s) + 2e^- = 2Hg(s) + SO_4^{2-}$ $E^0 = 0.615$ V

$$E_{cell} = E_{SCE} - \left(0.615 - \frac{0.0592}{2} \log [SO_4^{2-}] \right)$$

$$-0.106 = 0.244 - 0.613 + \frac{0.0592}{2} \log [SO_4^{2-}] = -0.371 - \frac{0.0592}{2} pSO_4$$

$$pSO_4 = (+0.106 - 0.371) 2 / 0.0592 = \underline{\underline{-8.95}}$$

23-13 $$\frac{[Hg(OAc)_2]}{[Hg^{2+}] [OAc^-]^2} = K_f = 2.7 \times 10^8$$

$Hg^{2+} + 2e^- \underset{\leftarrow}{\rightarrow} Hg(l)$ $E^0 = 0.854$ V

$$E = 0.854 - \frac{0.0592}{2} \log \frac{1}{[Hg^{2+}]} = 0.854 - \frac{0.0592}{2} \log \frac{K_f [OAc^-]^2}{[Hg(OAc)_2]}$$

When $[OAc^-]$ and $Hg(OAc)_2 = 1.00$, $E = E^0_{Hg(OAc)_2}$

$$E_{Hg(OAc)_2} = 0.854 - \frac{0.0592}{2} \log 2.7 \times 10^8 = \underline{\underline{0.604 \text{ V}}}$$

23-14 $CuY^{2-} + 2e \underset{\leftarrow}{\rightarrow} Cu(s) + Y^{4-}$ $E^0 = 0.13$ V $K_f = \frac{[CuY^{2-}]}{[Cu^{2+}] [Y^{4-}]}$

$Cu^{2+} + 2e \underset{\leftarrow}{\rightarrow} Cu(s)$ $E^0 = 0.337$ V

$$E = E^0 - \frac{0.0592}{2} \log \frac{1}{[Cu^{2+}]} = 0.337 - \frac{0.0592}{2} \log \frac{K_f [Y^{4-}]}{[CuY^{2-}]}$$

$$E = E^0_{CuY^{2-}} \quad \text{when} \quad [Y^{4-}] = [CuY^{2-}] = 1.00$$

$$0.13 = 0.337 - \frac{0.0592}{2} \log K_f$$

$$\log K_f = \frac{(0.337 - 0.13) \times 2}{0.0592} = 6.993$$

$$K_f = \underline{9.8 \times 10^2}$$

23-15
$$E = 0.244 - \left(0.21 - \frac{0.0592}{2} \log \frac{[Y^{4-}]}{2.61 \times 10^{-4}}\right)$$

(a)
$$E = 0.244 - 0.21 + \frac{0.0592}{2} \log \frac{0.121}{2.61 \times 10^{-4}} = \underline{\underline{0.113 \text{ V}}}$$

Proceeding in the same way we obtain

(b) $\underline{\underline{0.054 \text{ V}}}$ (c) $\underline{\underline{-0.005 \text{ V}}}$

23-16 $\text{pCu} = -\log [Cu^{2+}] = 2.488$

$$2.488 = -\frac{E_{cell} - K}{0.0592/2} = -\frac{0.124 - K}{0.0592/2} \qquad \text{(Equation 23-24)}$$

$$K = 2.488 \times \frac{0.0592}{2} + 0.124 = 0.1976$$

$$\text{pCu} = -\frac{0.105 - 0.1976}{0.0592/2} = \underline{3.13}$$

23-17 $Cd^{2+} + 2e^- \rightleftarrows Cd(s) \qquad E^0 = -0.403 \text{ V}$

$$CdX_2(s) + 2e^- \rightleftarrows Cd(s) + 2X^-$$

$$E_{cell} = 0.244 - \left(-0.403 - \frac{0.0592}{2} \log \frac{1}{[Cd^{2+}]}\right) = 0.647 + \frac{0.0592}{2} \log \frac{[X^-]^2}{K_{sp}}$$

$$1.020 = 0.647 + \frac{0.0592}{2} \log (0.02)^2 - \frac{0.0592}{2} \log K_{sp}$$

$$\log K_{sp} = \frac{(0.647 - 1.020 + 0.0592 \log 0.02) \, 2}{0.0592} = -16.0$$

$$K_{sp} = 1.0 \times 10^{-16}$$

23-18
$$0.515 = 0.244 - \left(0.000 - \frac{0.0592}{2} \log \frac{1.00}{[H^+]^2}\right)$$

$$0.515 - 0.244 = \frac{0.0592}{2} \log \frac{1}{[H^+]^2}$$

$$2.71 = -0.0592 \log [H^+]$$

$$\log [H^+] = -\frac{2.71}{0.0592} = -4.58$$

$$[H^+] = 2.64 \times 10^{-5}$$

$$K_a = \frac{(2.64 \times 10^{-5})0.300}{0.200} = 3.97 \times 10^{-5}$$

23-19 $2\,Ce^{4+} + HNO_2 + H_2O \rightleftharpoons 2Ce^{3+} + NO_3^- + 3H^+$

$$Ce^{4+} + e^- \rightleftharpoons Ce^{3+} \qquad E^0 = 1.44 \text{ V}$$

$$NO_3^- + 3H^+ + 2e \rightleftharpoons HNO_2 + H_2O \qquad E^0 = 0.94 \text{ V}$$

Initial no. mmol $HNO_2 = 40.00 \times 0.0500 = 2.000$

10.00 mL Ce^{4+} added

$$\text{no. mmol } NO_3^- \text{ formed} = 10.00 \times 0.0800 \text{ mmol } Ce^{4+} \times \frac{1 \text{ mmol } NO_3^-}{2 \text{ mmol } Ce^{4+}} = 0.4000$$

$$c_{NO_3^-} = \frac{0.4000 \text{ mmol } NO_3^-}{85.0 \text{ mL soln}} = 4.706 \times 10^{-3}$$

$$c_{HNO_2} = \frac{2.000 - 0.4000}{85} = 1.882 \times 10^{-2}$$

$$[H^+] = 1.00$$

Proceeding in the same way we obtain the data shown in the first two columns in the table that follows.

50.10 mL Ce^{4+} added

$$[Ce^{3+}] = \frac{2.000 \text{ mmol } HNO_2 \times 2 \text{ mmol } Ce^3 / \text{mol } HNO_2}{75.00 + 50.10} = 3.197 \times 10^{-2}$$

$$[Ce^{4+}] = \frac{(50.10 - 50.00) \times 0.08000}{75.00 + 50.10} = 6.395 \times 10^{-5}$$

$$E_{cell} = 1.44 - \frac{0.0592}{1} \log \frac{3.197 \times 10^{-2}}{6.395 \times 10^{-5}} - 0.244 = 1.336 \text{ V}$$

Proceeding in the same way, we find the data in the last two columns of the table.

Vol Ce^{4+}	E vs SCE	Vol Ce^{4+}	E vs SCE
10.00	0.68 V	50.10	1.04 V
25.00	0.70	51.00	1.10
40.00	0.71	55.00	1.14
49.00	0.75	60.00	1.16
49.9	0.78		

23-20 (a)
$$pH = 6.00 = -\frac{E_{cell} - K}{0.0592} = \frac{0.0412 + K}{0.0592} \qquad \text{(Equation 23-4)}$$

$$K = 0.314$$

$$pH = -\frac{-0.2004 - 0.314}{0.0592} = \frac{0.5144}{0.0592} = \underline{8.69}$$

$$[H^+] = \underline{\underline{2.05 \times 10^{-9}}}$$

(b) When $K = 0.315$, pH $= 8.706$, $[H^+] = 1.97 \times 10^{-9}$

When $K = 0.313$, pH $= 8.672$, $[H^+] = 2.13 \times 10^{-9}$

(c) error $1.97 \times 10^{-9} - 2.05 \times 10^{-9} = -8.0 \times 10^{-11}$

$$2.13 \times 10^{-9} - 2.05 \times 10^{-9} = +8.0 \times 10^{-11}$$

relative error $= \pm\dfrac{8.0 \times 10^{-11}}{2.05 \times 10^{-9}} = \pm 3.9\%$

23-21 (a) $pMg^{2+} = -\log 3.82 \times 10^{-3} = 2.479$

$$2.479 = -\frac{0.2714 - K}{0.0592/2} \qquad \text{(Equation 23-24)}$$

$$0.07338 = -0.2714 + K$$

$$K = 0.3448 = 0.345$$

$$pMg = -\frac{0.1901 - 0.345}{0.0592/2} = \underline{5.226}$$

$$[Mg^{2+}] = 5.95 \times 10^{-6}$$

(b) When $K = 0.347$, pMg $= 5.301$ and $[Mg^{2+}] = \underline{5.004 \times 10^{-6}}$

When $K = 0.343$, pMg = 5.166 and $[Mg^{2+}] = \underline{6.831 \times 10^{-6}}$

(c) error $= 5.004 \times 10^{-6} - 5.95 \times 10^{-6} = -9.5 \times 10^{-7}$

$\qquad 6.831 \times 10^{-6} - 5.95 \times 10^{-6} = +9.1 \times 10^{-7}$

relative error $= \dfrac{-9.5 \times 10^{-7} \times 100}{5.95 \times 10^{-6}} = \underline{\underline{-15.9}}$

$\qquad\qquad = \dfrac{9.1 \times 10^{-7} \times 100}{5.95 \times 10^{-6}} = \underline{\underline{+15.3}}$

23-22 We will write Equation 23-28 in the form

$$E_{cell} = K + 0.0592\, pA = K - 0.0592 \log [F^-]$$

Let c_x be the concentration of the diluted sample and c_s be the concentration of the added standard.

If -0.1823 V is the potential of the system containing the diluted sample only, we may write

$$-0.1823 = K - 0.0592 \log c_x$$

The concentration c_1 after the standard addition is

$$c_1 = \dfrac{25.0\, c_x + 5.00\, c_s}{30.0} = 0.833\, c_x + 0.1667\, c_s$$

and the potential -0.2446 V after the addition is given by

$$-0.2446 = K - 0.0592 \log (0.833\, c_x + 0.1667\, c_x)$$

Subtracting this equation from the first potential expression gives

$$0.0623 = -0.0592 \log \dfrac{c_x}{(0.833\, c_x + 0.1667\, c_s)}$$

$$\log \dfrac{c_x}{0.833\, c_x + 0.1667\, c_s} = -1.052$$

$$\dfrac{c_x}{0.833\, c_x + 0.1667\, c_s} = 0.0887$$

Since c_x and c_s appear in both the numerator and the denominator, we can substitute concentration in terms of mg F^- / mL rather than in molarity and write

$$c_x = 0.0887 \times 0.833\, c_x + 0.0887 \times 0.1667\, c_s$$

$$= 0.0739\, c_x + 0.0887 \times 0.1667 \times 0.00107 \text{ mg F}^-/\text{mL}$$

This equation rearranges to

$$c_x = \frac{1.582 \times 10^{-5} \text{ mg F}^-/\text{mL}}{1 - 0.0739} = 1.71 \times 10^{-5} \text{ mg F}^-/\text{mL}$$

$$\%\,\text{F}^- = \frac{1.71 \times 10^{-5} \,(\text{mg F}^-/\text{mL}) \times 100 \text{ mL} \times 10^{-3} \text{ g}/\text{mg}}{0.400 \text{ g sample}} \times 100\% = \underline{\underline{4.28 \times 10^{-4}\,\%}}$$

CHAPTER 24

24-1 (a)
$$E_{cell} = -0.126 - \frac{0.0592}{2}\log\frac{1}{0.125} - 0.000 + \frac{0.0592}{2}\log\frac{0.800}{(0.250)^2}$$

$$= -0.153 - (-0.033) = \underline{\underline{-0.120 \text{ V}}}$$

(b) $IR = 0.300 \times 0.95 = \underline{\underline{0.285 \text{ V}}}$

(c) $E_{applied} = -0.120 - 0.285 = \underline{\underline{-0.405 \text{ V}}}$

(d)
$$E_{applied} = -0.126 - \frac{0.0592}{2}\log\frac{1}{0.00100} + 0.033 - 0.285$$

$$= -0.215 + 0.033 - 0.285 = \underline{\underline{-0.467}}$$

24-2 (a) To lower M_1 to 1.00×10^{-4},

$$E_1 = E^0_{M_1} - \frac{0.0592}{2}\log\frac{1}{1.00 \times 10^{-4}} = E^0_{M_1} - 0.118 \text{ V}$$

M_2 begins to precipitate when

$$E_2 = E^0_{M_2} - 0.0592\log\frac{1}{0.200} = E^0_{M_2} - 0.414 \text{ V}$$

When $E_2 = E_1$, the concentration of M_1 will be reduced to $1.00 \times 10^{-4}\, M_1$ and M_2 will not have begun to precipitate. That is,

$$E^0_{M_2} - 0.041 = E^0_{M_1} - 0.118$$

$$E^0_{M_2} - E^0_{M_1} = \Delta E^0 = -0.118 + 0.0414 = \underline{\underline{-0.077 \text{ V}}}$$

	Charge on M_2	Charge on M_1	$\Delta E^0 = \mid E^0_{M_2} - E^0_{M_1} \mid$, V
(a)	1	2	$0.0414 - 0.118 = \underline{0.077}$
(b)	2	2	$0.0207 - 0.118 = \underline{0.097}$
(c)	3	1	$0.0138 - 0.237 = \underline{0.223}$
(d)	2	1	$0.0207 - 0.237 = \underline{0.216}$
(e)	2	3	$0.0207 - 0.0789 = \underline{0.0582}$

24-3 $Ag^+ + e^- \; \underset{\leftarrow}{\rightarrow} \; Ag(s)$ $E^0 \; = \; 0.799$ V

$Cu^{2+} + 2e^- \; \underset{\leftarrow}{\rightarrow} \; Cu(s)$ $E^0 \; = \; 0.337$ V

$BiO^+ + 2H^+ + 3e^- \; \underset{\leftarrow}{\rightarrow} \; Bi(s) + H_2O$ $E^0 \; = \; 0.320$ V

(a) We first calculate the potentials versus SCE to reduce the concentrations to 10^{-6} M. Thus,

For Ag^+

$$E_{cell} \; = \; 0.799 - 0.0592 \log \frac{1}{10^{-6}} - 0.244 \; = \; 0.444 - 0.244 \; = \; 0.200 \text{ V}$$

For BiO^+

$$E_{cell} \; = \; 0.320 - \frac{0.0592}{3} \log \frac{1}{10^{-6} \times (0.5)^2} - 0.244 \; = \; -0.054 \text{ V}$$

For Cu^{2+}

$$E_{cell} \; = \; 0.337 - \frac{0.0592}{2} \log \frac{1}{10^{-6}} - 0.244 \; = \; -0.085 \text{ V}$$

$Bi(s)$ begins to form when

$$E_{cell} \; = \; 0.320 - \frac{0.0592}{3} \log \frac{1}{0.055 \, (0.5)^2} - 0.244 \; = \; 0.041 \text{ V}$$

Cu^{2+} begins to precipitate when

$$E_{cell} \; = \; 0.337 - \frac{0.0592}{2} \log \frac{1}{0.175} - 0.244 \; = \; 0.071 \text{ V}$$

(b) Silver could be separated from BiO^+ and Cu^{2+} by keeping the cell potential greater than $+ 0.071$ V. Cu^{2+} and BiO^+ cannot be separated by controlled potential electrolysis.

24-4 We calculate the potentils at which the silver salts first form

For I^-, $E_{cell} = 0.244 - (-0.151 - 0.0592 \log 0.025) = 0.300$ V

For Br^-, $E_{cell} = 0.244 - (0.073 - 0.0592 \log 0.025) = 0.076$ V

For Cl^-, $E_{cell} = 0.244 - (0.151 - 0.0592 \log 0.025) = -0.002$ V

(a) AgI forms first at a potential of <u>0.300 V</u> - <u>galvanic</u> cell.

(b) When $[I^-] \leq 10^{-5}$

$$E_{cell} = 0.244 - (-0.151 - 0.0592 \log 10^{-5}) = 0.099 \text{ V}$$

$AgBr^-$ does not form until $E_{cell} = 0.076$. The <u>separation feasible</u> if E_{cell} is kept between 0.099 V and 0.076 V.

(c) I^- could be separated from Cl^- by maintaining the potential between 0.076 V and - 0.002 V.

(d) To separate AgBr quantitatively would require that

$$E_{cell} = 0.244 - (0.073 - 0.0592 \log 10^{-5}) = -0.125 \text{ V}$$

But AgCl forms at a potential of - 0.002 V. Therefore, <u>separation not feasible</u>.

24-5 (a) $E_{cell} = 0.854 - \dfrac{0.0592}{2} \log \dfrac{1}{10^{-6}} - 0.244 = \underline{\underline{0.432 \text{ V}}}$

(b) $K_f = 1.8 \times 10^7 = \dfrac{[Hg(SCN)_2]}{[Hg^{2+}][SCN^-]} = \dfrac{[Hg(SCN)_2]}{[Hg^{2+}] \, 0.100}$

$$[Hg(SCN)_2] + [Hg^{2+}] = 10^{-6}$$

Assume $[Hg^{2+}] << [Hg(SCN)_2]$

Substituting into the formation constant expression

$$1.8 \times 10^7 = \dfrac{1.00 \times 10^{-6}}{[Hg^{2+}]}$$

$$[Hg^{2+}] = 5.56 \times 10^{-14}$$

$$E_{cell} = 0.854 - \dfrac{0.0592}{2} \log \dfrac{1}{5.56 \times 10^{-14}} - 0.244 = \underline{\underline{0.218 \text{ V}}}$$

(c) Assume $[Hg^{2+}] + [HgBr_4^{2-}] \approx [HgBr_4^{2-}] = 1.00 \times 10^{-6}$

$$E_{\text{cell}} \;=\; 0.223 - \frac{0.0592}{2} \log \frac{[10^{-6}]}{(0.250)^4} - 0.244 \;=\; \underline{\underline{0.085 \text{ V}}}$$

To check the assumption we substitute 0.085 into the Nernst expression for Hg^{2+}.

$$0.085 \;=\; 0.854 - \frac{0.0592}{2} \log \frac{1}{[Hg^{2+}]} - 0.224$$

$$0.085 + 0.224 - 0.854 \;=\; \frac{0.0592}{2} \log [Hg^{2+}]$$

$$[Hg^{2+}] \;=\; 4 \times 10^{-19}$$

Thus the assumption that $[HgBr_4^{2-}] << [Hg^{2+}]$ is valid.

24-6 (a)

$$0.100 \text{ g Tl} \times \frac{1 \text{ mol Tl}}{204.37 \text{ g}} \times \frac{3 \text{ mol e}^-}{1 \text{ mol Tl}} \times 96485 \frac{C}{\text{mol e}^-} \;=\; 141.63 \text{ C}$$

$$141.63 \text{ C} \times \frac{1 \text{ A} \cdot \text{s}}{C} \times \frac{1}{0.80 \text{ A}} \times \frac{1 \text{ min}}{60 \text{ s}} \;=\; \underline{\underline{2.95 \text{ min}}}$$

(b) $2Tl^+ + 3H_2O \;\rightarrow\; Tl_2O_3 + 6H^+ + 4e^-$ (1/2) mol Tl^+ ≡ 1 mol e$^-$

$$0.100 \text{ g Tl}^+ \times \frac{1 \text{ mol Tl}^+}{204.37 \text{ g}} \times \frac{1 \text{ mol e}^-}{(1/2) \text{ mol Tl}^+} \times 96845 \frac{C}{\text{mol e}^-} \;=\; 94.42 \text{ C}$$

$$94.42 \text{ C} \times \frac{1 \text{ A} \cdot \text{s}}{C} \times \frac{1}{0.80 \text{ A}} \times \frac{1 \text{ min}}{60 \text{ s}} \;=\; \underline{\underline{1.97 \text{ min}}}$$

(c) Proceeding as in part (a)

$$\frac{0.100 \text{ g} \times \frac{1 \text{ mol}}{204.37 \text{ g}} \times 1 \text{ mol e}^-}{1 \text{ mol}} \times \frac{96485 \text{ C}}{\text{mol e}^-} \times \frac{1 \text{ A} \cdot \text{s}}{C} \times \frac{1}{0.80 \text{ A}} \times \frac{1 \text{ min}}{60 \text{ s}} \;=\; \underline{\underline{0.984 \text{ min}}}$$

24-7

$$11.63 \text{ C} \times \frac{1 \text{ mol e}^-}{96485 \text{ C}} \times \frac{2 \text{ mol CCl}_4}{2 \text{ mol e}^-} \;=\; 1.205 \times 10^{-4} \text{ mol CCl}_4$$

$$68.6 \times \frac{1 \text{ mol e}^-}{96485 \text{ C}} \times \frac{2 \text{ mol CHCl}_3}{6 \text{ mol e}^-} \;=\; 2.370 \times 10^{-4} \text{ mol CHCl}_3$$

original no. mol CHCl$_3$ $=\; 2.370 \times 10^{-4} - 1.205 \times 10^{-4} \;=\; 1.165 \times 10^{-4}$

$$\frac{1.205 \times 10^{-4} \text{ mol CCl}_4 \times 153.82 \text{ g CCl}_4 / \text{mol CCl}_4}{0.750 \text{ g sample}} \times 100\% \;=\; \underline{\underline{2.47\% \text{ CCl}_4}}$$

$$\frac{1.165 \times 10^{-4} \text{ mol } CHCl_3 \times 119.37 \text{ g } CHCl_3/\text{mol}}{0.750 \text{ g sample}} \times 100\% = \underline{\underline{1.85\% \; CHCl_3}}$$

24-8 $1 \text{ mol } As_2O_3 \equiv 2 \text{ mol } HaSO_3^{2-} \equiv 2 \text{ mol } I_2 \equiv 4 \text{ mol } e^-$

no. coulomb $= 0.1011 \text{ A} \times (12 \times 60 + 36) \text{ s} = 76.43 \text{ C}$

$$\text{wt } As_2O_3 = \frac{76.43 \text{ C}}{96485 \text{ C/mol } e^-} \times \frac{1 \text{ mol } As_2O_3}{4 \text{ mol } e^-} \times \frac{197.8 \text{ g}}{\text{mol}} \; As_2O_3$$

$$= 0.03917 \text{ g } As_2O_3$$

$$\% \; As_2O_3 = \frac{0.03917 \text{ g } As_2O_3}{6.39 \text{ g sample}} \times 100 = 0.613\%$$

24-9 The equivalent weight of an acid is that weight that contains one mole of titratable H^+.

$$0.0324 \text{ A} \times 251 \text{ s} \times \frac{1 \text{ C}}{A \cdot s} \times \frac{1 \text{ F}}{96485 \text{ C}} \times \frac{1 \text{ equiv HA}}{F} = 8.429 \times 10^{-5} \text{equiv/HA}$$

$$\frac{0.0809 \text{ g HA}}{8.429 \times 10^{-4} \text{ equiv HA}} = \underline{\underline{960 \text{ g/equiv}}}$$

24-10 $1 \text{ mol } C_6H_5NH_2 \equiv 3 \text{ mol } Br_2 \equiv 6 \text{ mol } e^-$

$$(3.76 - 0.27) \text{ min} \times \frac{60 \text{ s}}{\text{min}} \times 1.00 \times 10^{-3} \frac{C}{s} \times \frac{\text{mol } e^-}{96485 \text{ C}} \times \frac{1 \text{ mol } C_6H_5NH_2}{6 \text{ mol } e^-} = 3.617 \times 10^{-7} \text{ mol } C_6H_5NH_2$$

$$3.617 \times 10^{-7} \text{ mol } C_6H_5NH_2 \times 93.128 \frac{\text{g } C_6H_5NH_2}{\text{mol } C_6H_5NH_2} \times 10^6 \; \mu g/g = \underline{\underline{33.7 \; \mu g \; C_6H_5NH_2}}$$

CHAPTER 25

25-1 (a) Voltammetry is an analytical technique that is based upon measuring the current that develops in a micro-electrode as the applied potential is varied. Polarography is a particular type of voltammetry in which the microelectrode is a dropping mercury electrode.

(b) In linear scan polarography, current in a cell containing a dropping mercury electrode is monitored continuously as applied potential is increased at a constant rate. In pulse polarography, an excitation signal is used that consists of a series of pulses that increase in size linearly as a function of time. The pulses are applied during the last few milliseconds of the life of a drop. The current is increased during this period.

(c) As shown in Figure 25-27 (page 662) and 25-30 (page 664) differential pulse polarography and square wave polarography differ in the type of pulse sequence used.

(d) In the dropping mercury electrode, mercury is forced through a fine capillary tubing leading to a continuous stream of identical drops that typically have a lifetime of two to six seconds. A hanging drop consists of a single mercury drop that is not dislodged until the end of the experiment.

(e) A residual current in polarography is a nonfaradaic charging current that arises form the flow of electrons required to charge individual drops of mercury as they form and fall. A limiting current is a constant faradaic current that is limited to magnitude by the rate at which a reactant is brought to the surface of a microelectrode.

(f) In voltammetry, a limiting current is a constant current that is independent of applied potential. Its magnitude is limited by the rate at which a reactant is brought to the surface of the electrode by diffusion, migration, and convection. A diffusion current is a limiting current when analyte transport by migration and convection has been eliminated.

(g) Turbulent flow is a type of liquid flow that has no regular pattern. Laminar flow is a type of liquid flow in which layers of liquid slide by one another in a direction that is parallel to a solid surface.

(h) The difference between the half-wave potential and the standard potential for a reversible reaction is shown by Equation 25-22. That is,

$$E_{1/2} = E_A^0 - \frac{0.0592}{n} \log \frac{k_A}{k_P} - E_{ref}$$

where k_A and k_P are constants that are proportional to the diffusion coefficients of the analyte and product and E_{ref} is the potential of the reference electrode.

(i) In normal stripping methods, the analyte is deposited on a mercury drop by electrolysis. In adsorption stripping methods, the analyte is deposited by physical adsorption on the mercury drop. The deposited analyte is determined in the same way by the two methods.

25-2 (a) Voltammograms are plots of current as a function of voltage applied to a microelectrode.

(b) Hydrodynamic voltammetry is a type of voltammetry in which the analyte solution is vigorously stirred or caused to flow by a microelectrode thus causing the reactant to be brought to the electrode surface by convection as well as diffusion.

(c) The Nernst diffusion layer is the thin layer of stagnant solution that is immediately adjacent to the surface of an electrode.

(d) A mercury film electrode is formed by depositing a thin film of mercury on a small solid metal or graphite surface.

(e) The half-wave potential is the potential on a voltammetric wave at which the current is one half of the limiting current.

25-3 Most organic electrode processes involve hydrogen ions. A typical reaction is

$$R + nH^+ + ne^- \rightarrow RH_n$$

where R and RH_n are the oxidized and reduced forms of the organic molecule. Unless buffered solutions are used, marked pH charges will occur at the electrode surface. Because the reduction potential (and sometimes the product) is affected by pH, drawn out and poorly defined waves are observed.

25-4 The advantages of the dropping mercury electrode compared with other types of microelectrodes include: (1) its high hydrogen overvoltage, (2) its continuously produced fresh metal surface, and (3) its reproducible average currents that are immediately realized at any given applied potential. The disadvantages include: (1) its poor anodic potential range, (2) its relative large residual currents, (3) its tendency to yield current maxima, and (4) its inconvenience.

25-5 A plot of $E_{applied}$ versus $\log \frac{i}{i_d - i}$ will yield a straight line having a slope of $-0.0592/n$. Thus n is readily

computed from the slope.

25-6 For the reduction of quinone (Q) to hydroquinone (H_2Q), Equation 25-3 takes the form

$$E_{appl} = E_Q^0 - \frac{0.0592}{n} \log \frac{c_{H_2Q}^0}{c_Q^0 \left(c_{H^+}^0\right)^2} - E_{ref}$$

where $c_{H^+}^0$ is the concentration of H^+ at the electrode surface. Substituting Equations 25-8 and 25-10 into this equation gives

$$E_{appl} = E_Q^0 - \frac{0.0592}{n} \log \frac{k_Q}{k_{H_2Q}\left(c_{H^+}^0\right)^2} - \frac{0.0592}{n} \log \frac{i}{i_l - i} - E_{ref}$$

When $i = i_l/2$, E_{appl} is the half-wave potential. With the added assumption that $k_Q \approx k_{H_2Q}$, the foregoing equation becomes

$$E_{1/2} = E_Q^0 - E_{ref} - \frac{0.0592}{n} \log \frac{1}{\left(c_{H^+}^0\right)^2} \quad (1)$$

$$= 0.599 - 0.244 - 0.0592 \, pH = 0.355 - 0.0592 \, pH$$

(a) At pH 4.00,

$$E_{1/2} = 0.355 - 0.0592 \times 7.00 = \underline{\underline{-0.059 \text{ V}}}$$

(b) Similarly at pH 5.00, $E_{1/2} = \underline{\underline{+0.059 \text{ V}}}$

25-7 In linear scan polarography the residual currents result from trace impurities but more important from a charging current in which each mercury drop is charged and carries this charge down to the bottom of the cell when the drop breaks off from the capillary.

In current sampled polarography, current measurements are made at only the end of the drop lifetime so that large fluctuations in the current are eliminated. This technique does not eliminate the charging current but the decrease in fluctuations make it possible to determine the residual current more accurately.

25-8 (a)
$$31.3 \times 10^{-6}\ A \times 5\ min \times 60\ \frac{s}{min} \times \frac{1\ C}{A \cdot s} \times \frac{1\ mol\ e^-}{96485\ C} = 9.732 \times 10^{-8}\ mol\ e^-$$

$$9.732 \times 10^{-8}\ mol\ e^- \times \frac{1\ mol\ Cd^{2+}}{2\ mol\ e^-} = 4.866 \times 10^{-8}\ mol\ Cd\ deposits$$

$$20.0\ mL \times 10^{-3}\ \frac{L}{mL} \times 3.65 \times 10^{-3}\ \frac{mol\ Cd^{2+}}{L} = 7.30 \times 10^{-5}\ mol\ Cd^{2+}\ originally$$

$$\%\ decrease\ in\ [Cd^{2+}] = \frac{4.866 \times 10^{-8}}{7.30 \times 10^{-5}} \times 100 = \underline{\underline{0.067\%}}$$

(b) At 10 min, % decrease = $0.067 \times 10/5$ = <u>0.13%</u>

(c) At 30 min, % decrease = $0.067 \times 30/5$ = <u>0.40%</u>

25-9
$$c_{std} = 2.00 \times 10^{-3}\ \frac{mol}{mL} \times \frac{112.4\ mg\ Cd}{mmol} = 0.2248\ \frac{mg\ Cd}{mL}$$

When $V_{std} = 0$, $(i_d)_x = k\ V_x c_x / 50.0$

When std present, $(i_d)_{std} = k\ (V_x c_x + 0.2248\ V_s) / 50.0$

Solving these two equations simultaneously gives

$$c_x = \frac{0.2248\ V_x\ (i_d)_x}{V_x\ [(i_d)_{std} - (i_d)_x]}$$

Substituting into this equation gives for mg Cd/mL

(a) <u>0.369</u>   (b) <u>0.346</u>   (c) <u>0.144</u>   (d) <u>0.314</u>

25-10 A plot of $E_{1/2}$ versus log M is linear as predicted by Equation 25-21.

A least-squares treatment of the data leads to the equation

$$E_{1/2} = -0.605\ \log M - 0.578$$

From Equation 25-21, the slope m is given by

$$m = -0.0605 = -0.0592\ x/n$$

$$x = 0.0605/(0.0592/2) = 2.0$$

Thus, the complex is **PbA$_2$**.

When [M] = 1.00, $E_{1/2} = -0.578$ and Equation 25-21 takes the form

$$-0.578 - (-0.405) = -\frac{0.0592}{2}\log K_f - \frac{0.0592}{n}\log 1.00$$

$$\log K_f = 5.845 \quad\text{and}\quad K_f = \underline{\underline{7.0 \times 10^5}}$$

25-11 At about +0.1 V, the following anodic reaction begins

$$2Hg + 2Br^- \rightarrow Hg_2Br_2(s) + 2e^-$$

A limiting current for this reaction then occurs in the region of approximately +0.17 to +0.48 V, whereupon oxidation of the mercury leads to very large currents. That is,

$$2Hg \rightarrow Hg_2^{2+} + 2e^-$$

The wave at 0.12 V is useful for determination of Br$^-$. The diffusion current should be directly proportional to [Br$^-$].

25-12 If we assume that the diffusion coefficient for Ox and R are about the same, equation (1) in Solution 25-6 becomes

$$E_{1/2} = E_{Ox}^0 - E_{ref} - \frac{0.0592}{4}\log\frac{1}{\left(c_{H^+}^0\right)^4}$$

$$= K - 0.0592\,\text{pH}$$

When pH = 2.5, $E_{1/2} = -0.349$. Thus

$$K = -0.349 + 0.0592 \times 2.5 = -0.201$$

(a) At pH = 1.00, $E_{1/2} = -0.201 - 0.0592 \times 1.00 = \underline{\underline{-0.260\text{ V}}}$

(b) At pH = 3.5, $E_{1/2} = -0.201 - 0.0592 \times 3.5 = \underline{\underline{-0.408\text{ V}}}$

(c) At pH = 7.0, $E_{1/2} = -0.201 - 0.0592 \times 7.0 = \underline{\underline{-0.615\text{ V}}}$

25-13 Stripping methods are generally more sensitive than other voltammetic procedures because the analyte can be removed from a relatively large volume of solution and concentrated on a tiny electrode for a long period (often many minutes). After concentration, the potential is reversed and all of the analyte that has been stored on the electrode is rapidly oxidized or reduced producing a large current.

117

25-14 The advantage of voltammetry at ultramicroelectrodes include: (1) their low *IR* loss that permits their use in low-dielectric-constant solvents, such as hydrocarbons, (2) their small size that permits electrochemical studies on exceedingly small samples, such as the inside of living organs, and (3) their great speed of equilibration even in unstirred solution.

CHAPTER 26

26-1 (a) *Elution* is a process in which species are washed through a chromatographic column by additions of fresh solvent.

(b) The *mobile phase* in chromatography is the one that moves over or through an immobilized phase that is fixed in place in a column or on the surface of a flat plate.

(c) The *stationary phase* in a chromatographic column is a solid or liquid that is fixed in place. A mobile phase then passes over or through the stationary phase.

(d) The *distribution constant K* in chromatography is the ratio of the concentration of the analyte in the stationary phase to its concentration in the mobile phase when equilibrium exists between the two phases.

(e) The *retention time* for an analyte is the time interval between its injection onto a column and the appearance of its peak at the other end of the column.

(f) The *retention factor k'* is defined by the equation

$$k' = K_A V_S / V_M$$

where K_A is the distribution constant for species A and V_S and V_M are the volumes of the stationary and mobile phases respectively.

(g) The *selectivity factor* α of a column toward two species is given by $\alpha = K_B / K_A$ where K_B is the distribution constant for the more strongly held species and K_A is the corresponding constant for the less strongly held species.

(h) The *plate height H* of a chromatographic column is defined by the relationship

$$H = \sigma^2 / L$$

where σ^2 is the variance obtained from the Gaussian shaped chromatographic peak and L is the length of the column packing in cm.

(i) *Longitudinal diffusion* is a source of band broadening in a column in which a solute diffuses from the concentrated center of a band to the more dilute regions on either side. This movement is thus toward and opposed to the direction of flow of the mobile phase.

(j) *Eddy diffusion* is a phenomenon in which molecules of an analyte reach the end of a column at different times as consequence of traveling through the column by pathways that differ in length.

(k) The *resolution R_s* of a column toward two species A and B is given by the equation $R_s = 2\Delta Z/(W_A + W_B)$ where ΔZ is the distance (in units of time) between the peaks for the two species and W_A and W_B are the widths (also in units of time) of the peaks at their bases.

(l) The *eluent* in chromatography is the fresh mobile phase that carries the analyte through the column.

26-2 The *general elution problem* arises whenever chromatograms are obtained on samples that contain species with widely different partition ratios. When conditions are such that good separations of the more strongly held species are realized, lack of resolution among the weakly retained species is observed. Conversely, when conditions are chosen that give satisfactory separations of the weakly retained compounds, severe band broadening and long retention times are encountered for the strongly bound species. The general elution problem is often solved in liquid chromatography by gradient elution; temperature programming serves the same purpose in gas chromatography.

26-3 The variables that lead to *zone broadening* include: (1) large particle diameters for stationary phases; (2) large column diameters; (3) high temperatures (important only in gas chromatography); (4) for liquid stationary phases, thick layers of the immobilized liquid; and (5) very rapid or very slow flow rates.

26-4 In gas-liquid chromatography, the mobile phase is a gas, whereas in liquid-liquid chromatography it is a liquid.

26-5 In liquid-liquid chromatography, the stationary phase is a liquid which is immobilized by adsorption or chemical bonding to a solid surface. The equilibria that cause separation are distribution equilibria between two immiscible liquid phases. In liquid-solid chromatography, the stationary phase is a solid surface and the equilibria involved are adsorption equilibria.

26-6 Variables that affect the selectivity factor α include the composition of the mobile phase, column temperature, composition of the stationary phase, and chemical interaction between the stationary phase and one of the solutes being separated.

26-7 In gas chromatography, the capacity factor is varied by changing the column temperature (temperature programming). In liquid chromatography, variation is accomplished by altering the composition of the solvent (gradient elution).

26-8 The number of plates in a column can be determined by measuring the retention time t_R and width of a peak at its base W. The number of plates N is then given by the equation $N = 16(t_R/W)^2$.

26-9 In gas chromatography temperature increases result in shorter elution times but poorer resolution of similar species. Small temperature variations have little effect in liquid chromatography.

26-10 The minima observed in plots of plate height versus flow rate are caused by longitudinal diffusion, which in contrast to other broadening sources, goes on to a greater extent at low flow rates than at high. The rate of longitudinal diffusion is, however, orders of magnitude larger in a gaseous mobile phase than in a liquid. Thus, the phenomenon becomes noticeable at higher flow rates in gases than in liquids.

26-11 Gradient elution is a method of performing liquid chromatography in which the composition of the mobile phase is changed continuously or in steps in order to optimize separations.

26-12 $N = 16(t_R/W)^2$ (Equation 26 – 17)

(a)

		N	N^2
A	$16(5.4/0.41)^2 =$	2775.49	7.703349×10^6
B	$16(13.3/1.07)^2 =$	2472.04	6.11099×10^6
C	$16(14.1/1.16)^2 =$	2363.97	5.58836×10^6
D	$16(21.6/1.72)^2 =$	2523.32	6.367093×10^6
	$\sum N =$	10134.81	$\sum N^2 = 25.76979 \times 10^6$

$$\overline{N} = 10134.81/5 = 2533.70 = \underline{2.53 \times 10^3}$$

(b)
$$s = \sqrt{\frac{25.76979 \times 10^6 - (10134.81)^2/4}{4-1}} = 174 = 0.2 \times 10^3$$

$$\overline{N} = \underline{\underline{2.5(\pm 0.2) \times 10^3}}$$

(c) $H = 24.7\,\text{cm}/2534\,\text{plates} = 9.747 \times 10^{-3} = \underline{\underline{0.0097\,\text{cm}}}$

26-13 (a) $k' = (t_R - t_M)/t_M$ (Equation 26 – 8, page 680)

A $k'_A = (5.4 - 3.1)/3.1 = 0.742 = \underline{0.74}$

B $k'_B = (13.3 - 3.1)/3.1 = 3.29 = \underline{\underline{3.3}}$

C $k'_C = (14.1 - 3.1)/3.1 = 3.55 = \underline{\underline{3.5}}$

D $k'_D = (21.6 - 3.1)/3.1 = 5.97 = \underline{6.0}$

(b) Rearranging Equation 26-5 (page 680) yields

$$K = k'V_M/V_S$$

Substituting the equation in part (a) and the numerical data for V_M and V_S gives

$$K = [(t_R - t_M)/t_M]\,1.37/0.164 = [(t_R - t_M)/t_M]\,8.35$$

and

$$K_A = [(5.4 - 3.1)/3.1]\,8.35 = \underline{6.2}$$

$$K_B = [(13.3 - 3.1)/3.1]\,8.35 = \underline{\underline{27}}$$

$$K_C = [(14.1 - 3.1)/3.1]\,8.35 = \underline{\underline{30}}$$

$$K_D = [(21.6 - 3.1)/3.1]\,8.35 = \underline{\underline{50}}$$

26-14 $R_S = 2[(t_R)_C - (t_R)_B]/(W_B + W_C)$ \qquad (Equation 26 – 20, page 688)

(a) $R_S = 2(14.1 - 13.3)/(1.07 + 1.16) = 0.717 = \underline{\underline{0.72}}$

(b)
$$\alpha_{C,B} = \frac{(t_R)_C - t_M}{(t_R)_B - t_M} \qquad \text{(Equation 26 – 11, page 680)}$$

$$= \frac{14.1 - 3.1}{13.3 - 3.1} = \underline{\underline{1.08}}$$

(c) Proceeding as in Example 26-1d, (page 690), we write

$$\frac{(R_S)_1}{(R_S)_2} = \frac{\sqrt{N_1}}{\sqrt{N_2}} = \frac{0.717}{1.5} = \frac{\sqrt{2534}}{\sqrt{N_2}}$$

$$N_2 = 2534 \times (1.5)^2/(0.717)^2 = 11090 \text{ plates}$$

From Solution 26-12, $H = 9.747 \times 10^{-3}$ cm/plate

$$L = 9.747 \times 10^{-3} \times 11090 \times 10^{-3} = \underline{\underline{108 \text{ cm}}}$$

(d) Proceeding as in Example 26-1e,

$$\frac{(t_R)_1}{(t_R)_2} = \frac{(R_S)_1^2}{(R_S)_2^2} = \frac{14.1}{(t_R)_2} = \frac{(0.717)^2}{(1.5)^2}$$

$$(t_R)_2 = 14.1\,(1.5)^2/(0.717)^2 = 61.7 = \underline{\underline{62 \text{ min}}}$$

26-15 (a) From Equation 26-20 (page 688),

$$R_S = 2\,[(t_R)_D - (t_R)_C]/(W_D + W_C)$$

$$= 2(21.6 - 14.1)/(1.72 + 1.16) = 5.21 = \underline{\underline{5.2}}$$

(b) Proceeding as in part (d) of the Example 26-1 (page 690), we write

$$N_1 = N_2 \frac{(R_S)_1^2}{(R_S)_2^2} = 2534 \times \frac{(1.5)^2}{(5.21)^2} = 210 \text{ plates}$$

$$L = 210 \text{ plates} \times 9.75 \times 10^{-3} \text{ cm/plate} = \underline{\underline{2.1 \text{ cm}}}$$

26-16 $N = 16\,(t_R/W)^2$ \qquad (Equation 26 – 17, page 683)

Letting methylcyclohexane be A, methylcyclohexene be B, and toluene be C,

	N_i	N_i^2
N_A	$16(10.0/0.76)^2 = 2770.08$	7.67336×10^6
N_B	$16(10.9/0.82)^2 = 2827.13$	7.99265×10^6
N_C	$16(13.4/1.06)^2 = 2556.92$	6.53786×10^6
	$\sum N_i = 8154.13$	$\sum N_i^2 = 22.20387 \times 10^6$

(a) $\overline{N} = 8154.13/3 = 2718 = \underline{2.72 \times 10^3 \text{ plates}}$

(b)

$$s = \sqrt{\frac{22.20387 \times 10^6 - (8154.13)^2/3}{3-1}} = 142 \text{ plates}$$

$$s_m = 142/\sqrt{3} = 82 = \underline{0.08 \times 10^3} \qquad \text{(Equation a1 - 17, page A - 9)}$$

$$\overline{N} = 2.72 \times 10^3 \ (\pm 0.08 \times 10^3) \text{ plates}$$

(c) $H = 40/2718 = 1.47 \times 10^{-2} = \underline{0.015 \text{ cm/plate}}$

26-17 (a) Substituting into Equation 26-20 (page 688)

$$R_S = 2(10.9 - 10.0)/(0.79 + 0.82) = 1.14 = \underline{1.1}$$

(b) $R_S = 2(13.4 - 10.9)/(0.82 + 1.06) = 2.66 = \underline{2.7}$

(c) $R_S = 2(13.4 - 10.0)/(1.06 + 0.76) = 3.74 = \underline{3.7}$

26-18 (a) Proceeding as in part (d) of Example 26-1, we write

$$\frac{N_1}{N_2} = \frac{(R_S)_1^2}{(R_S)_2^2} = \frac{2718}{N_2} = \frac{(1.14)^2}{(1.5)^2}$$

$$N_2 = 4706 = \underline{4.7 \times 10^3 \text{ plates}}$$

(b) From Solution 26-16(c), $H = 1.47 \times 10^{-2}$ cm/plate

$$L = 4706 \times 1.47 \times 10^{-2} = 69.1 \text{ cm} = \underline{\underline{69 \text{ cm}}}$$

(c) Proceeding as in part (e) of Example 26-1, we write

$$\frac{(t_R)_1}{(t_R)_2} = \frac{(R_S)_1^2}{(R_S)_2^2} = \frac{(1.14)^2}{(1.5)^2} = \frac{10.9}{(t_R)_2}$$

$$(t_R)_2 = 18.9 = \underline{\underline{19 \text{ min}}}$$

26-19 (a) $k_1' = (10.0 - 1.9)/1.9 = 4.26 = \underline{\underline{4.3}}$ (Equation 26 – 8)

$k_2' = (10.9 - 1.9)/1.9 = 4.74 = \underline{\underline{4.7}}$

$k_3' = (13.4 - 1.9)/1.9 = 6.053 = \underline{\underline{6.1}}$

(b) Rearranging Equation 26-5 and substituting numerical values for V_M and V_S gives

$K_1 = 4.26 \times 62.6/19.6 = 1.366 = \underline{\underline{14}}$

$K_2 = 4.74 \times 62.6/19.6 = 1.51 = \underline{\underline{15}}$

$K_3 = 6.05 \times 62.6/19.6 = 1.93 = \underline{\underline{19}}$

(c) $\alpha_{2,1} = (10.9 - 1.9)/(10.0 - 1.9) = \underline{\underline{1.11}}$ (Equation 26 – 11)

(d) $\alpha_{3,2} = (13.4 - 1.9)/(10.9 - 1.9) = \underline{\underline{1.28}}$

26-20 (a) Variables that lead to band broadening: (1) very low or very high flow rates; (2) high viscosity mobile phases; (3) low temperatures; (4) large particle sizes for packing; (5) for liquid stationary phases, thick films; (6) long columns; (7) slow introduction of sample; (8) large samples.

(b) Variables that lead to band separation: (1) packings that produce partition coefficients that differ significantly; (2) increases the length of the column packing; (3) variations in mobile phase composition; (4) choice of an optimum temperature; (5) changes in pH of the mobile phase; (6) incorporation of a species in the stationary phases that selectively complexes certain analytes.

26-21 Slow sample introduction leads to band broadening.

26-22 (a) $k_M' = K_M V_S / V_M = 6.01 \times 0.422 = \underline{\underline{2.54}}$ (Equation 26 – 5)

$k_N' = 6.20 \times 0.422 = \underline{\underline{2.62}}$

(b) $\alpha = 6.20/6.01 = \underline{\underline{1.03}}$ (Equation 26 – 10)

(c) Substituting into Equation 26-22 gives

$$N = 16(1.5)^2 \left(\frac{1.03}{1.03 - 1.00}\right)^2 \left(\frac{1.00 + 2.62}{2.62}\right)^2 = \underline{\underline{8.1 \times 10^4 \text{ plates}}}$$

(d) $L = 8.1 \times 10^4 \times 2.2 \times 10^{-3} = 178 = \underline{\underline{1.8 \times 10^2 \text{ cm}}}$

(e) Substituting into Equation 26-25 gives

$$(t_R)_N = \frac{16(1.5)^2 \times 2.2 \times 10^{-3}}{7.10} \left(\frac{1.03}{1.03 - 1.00}\right)^2 \frac{(3.62)^3}{(2.62)^2} = \underline{\underline{91 \text{ min}}}$$

26-23 (a) $V_S/V_M = 0.422$

$$k'_M = K_M V_S/V_M = 6.01 \times 0.422 = 2.54 \qquad \text{(Equation } 26-5\text{)}$$

$$k'_N = 6.20 \times 0.422 = 2.62$$

(b) $\alpha = 6.20/6.01 = 1.03$

(c) $$N = 16(1.5)^2 \left(\frac{1.03}{1.03-1.00}\right)^2 \left(\frac{1.00+2.62}{2.62}\right)^2 = \underline{\underline{8.1 \times 10^4 \text{ plates}}} \qquad \text{(Equation } 26-22\text{)}$$

(d) $$L = 8.1 \times 10^4 \times 2.2 \times 10^{-3} = \underline{\underline{1.8 \times 10^2 \text{cm}}}$$

(e) $$(t_R)_N = \frac{16(1.5)^2 \times 2.2 \times 10^{-3}}{7.10} \left(\frac{1.03}{1.03-1.00}\right)^2 \frac{(3.62)^3}{(2.62)^2} = \underline{\underline{18 \text{ min}}}$$

26-24

Compound	Peak Area	Response Factor, F	Area $\times F$	% Compound
Methyl acetate	17.6	0.65	11.44	14.83
Methyl propionate	44.7	0.83	37.10	48.09
Methyl n-butyrate	31.1	0.92	28.61	37.08
			77.15	100.00

26-25

Compound	Peak Area	Response Factor, F	Area $\times F$	% Compound
1	27.6	0.70	19.32	14.99
2	32.4	0.72	23.33	18.10
3	47.1	0.75	35.33	27.41
4	40.6	0.73	29.64	22.99
5	27.3	0.78	21.29	16.52
			128.91	100.1

CHAPTER 27

27-1 In *gas-liquid chromatography*, the stationary phase is a liquid that is immobilized on a solid. Retention of sample constituents involves equilibria between a gaseous and a liquid phase. In gas-solid chromatography, the stationary phase is a solid surface that retains analytes by physical adsorption. Here separations involve adsorption equilibria.

27-2 Gas-solid chromatography is used primarily for separating low-molecular-weight gaseous species, such as carbon dioxide, carbon monoxide, and oxides of nitrogen.

27-3 Gas-solid chromatography has limited application because active or polar compounds are retained more or less permanently on the packings. In addition severe tailing is often observed owing to the nonlinear character of the physical adsorption process.

27-4 (a) Retention volume V_R is defined by the equation

$$V_R = t_R F$$

where t_R is the retention time and F is the volumetric flow rate.

(b) The corrected retention volume V_R^0 is the retention volume after correction to the average pressure within the column. It is given by

$$V_R^0 = j t_R F$$

where j is the pressure correction factor given by Equation 27-5, page 702.

(c) The specific retention volume V_g is defined by the equation

$$V_g = \frac{V_R^0 - V_M^0}{W} \times \frac{273}{T_c}$$

where V_M is the retention volume of a species that is not retained by the stationary phase, W is the mass of the stationary phase and T_c is the column temperature in kelvins.

27-5 In a soap bubble meter, a soap film is formed in a gas buret through which the effluent from a gas-chromatographic column is flowing. The flow rate is then determined from the time required for the film to travel between two of the graduations in the buret.

27-6 *Temperature programming* involves increasing the temperature of a gas-chromatographic column as a function of time. This technique is particularly useful for samples that contain constituents whose boiling points differ significantly. Low boiling point constituents are separated initially at temperatures that provide good resolution. As the separation proceeds, the column temperature is increase so that the higher boiling constituents come off the column with good resolution and at reasonable lengths of time.

27-7 A concentration-sensitive detector responds to the concentration of the analyte in the mobile phase, whereas a mass-sensitive responds to the number of analyte molecules or ions that come in contact with the detector. Peak areas for a concentration-sensitive detector increase as the flow rate decreases because the analyte is in contact with the detector for a longer period. Peak areas for a mass-sensitive detector are not greatly affected by flow rate. Using CS for concentration sensitive and MS for mass sensitive, we find for each of the detectors listed (a) CS, (b) MS, (c) MS, (d) CS, (e) MS, (f) MS.

27-8 (a) The thermal conductivity detector is based upon the decrease in thermal conductivity of the helium or hydrogen carrier gas brought about by the presence of analyte molecules.

(b) The atomic emission detector is based upon the intensity of atomic emission lines generated from certain of the elements contained in analyte molecules. Atomization of the analyte and excitation of atomic spectra is brought about by passing the eluent through an energetic microwave field.

(c) The thermionic detector is based upon the ion currents produced when the mobile phase is combusted in a hydrogen flame and then passed over a heated rubidium silicate bead. It is used primarily for detecting analytes that contain phosphorus or nitrogen.

(d) The electron-capture detector is based upon the attenuation by analyte molecules of a standing ion current generated in the effluent by ionization of mobile phase molecules with a β emitter. Electronegative functional groups are particularly effective at capturing electrons and thus reducing the ion current.

(e) The flame photometric detector is based upon the radiation emitted by sulfur and phosphorus containing molecules when the eluent is passed into a low-temperature hydrogen/air flame.

(f) The photoionization detector is based upon the ion currents that develop when analyte molecules are irradiated with an intense beam of far-ultraviolet radiation.

27-9 (a) Advantages, thermal conductivity: general applicability, large linear range simplicity, nondestructive. Disadvantage: low sensitivity.

(b) Advantages, atomic emission: selectivity, large linear range, high sensitivity, general applicability. Disadvantages: destructive, high equipment cost.

(c) Advantage, thermionic: high sensitivity for compounds containing nitrogen and phosphorus, good linear range. Disadvantages: destructive, not applicable for many types of analytes.

(d) Advantages, electron capture: high sensitivity and selectivity toward analytes with electronegative functional group, nondestructive. Disadvantages: nonlinear response under some circumstances, limited response range.

(e) Advantages, flame photometric: selective toward sulfur and phosphorus containing analytes, good sensitivity. Disadvantages: destructive, limited applicability.

(f) Advantages, photoionization: versatility, nondestructive, large linear range.

27-10 Diatomaceous earth particles having diameters ranging from 250 to 170 μm or 170 to 149 μm.

27-11 (a) A PLOT column is a porous layer open tubular column, which is also called a support coated open tubular (SCOT) column. The inner surface of a PLOT column is lines with a thin film of a support material, such as a diatomaceous earth. This type of column holds several times as much stationary phase as does a wall-coated column.

(b) A WCOT column is simply a capillary tubing fashioned from fused silica stainless steel, aluminum, copper, plastic, or glass. Its inner wall are coated with a thin layer of the mobile phase.

(c) The SCOT column is described in the answer to part (a) of this question.

27-12 Megapore columns are open tubular columns that have a greater inside diameter (530 µm) than typical open tubular columns, which range in diameter from 150 to 320 µm.

27-13 Fused silica columns have greater physical strength and flexibility than glass open tubular columns and are less reactive toward analytes than either glass or metal columns.

27-14 Desirable properties of a stationary phase for GLC include: low volatility, thermal stability, chemical inertness, and solvent characteristics that provide suitable k' and α values for the various analytes to be separated.

27-15 Currently, liquid stationary phases are generally bonded and/or cross-linked in order to provide thermal stability and a more permanent stationary phase that will not leach off the column. Bonding involves attaching a monomolecular layer of the stationary phase to the packing surface by means of chemical bonds. Cross linking involves treating the stationary phase while it is in the column with a chemical reagent that creates cross links between the molecules making up the stationary phase.

27-16 Film thickness of stationary phases influences the rate at which analytes are carried through the column with the rate increasing as the thickness is decreased. Less band broadening is encountered with thin films.

27-17 The retention index for an analyte is a measure of the rate at which it is carried through a column compared with the rate of movement of two normal alkanes one that moves faster than the analyte and the other that moves more slowly. To obtain the retention index of an analyte on a given column, the log of the adjusted retention times for the two alkanes and the analyte are determined. The retention index of the two alkanes is, by definition, 100 times the number of carbon atoms they contain. Thus, the retention index for butane is always 400 and for pentane 500. The retention index for the analyte is then derived by interpolation between the two logarithmic retention indexes of the alkanes (see solution to Problem 27-20).

27-18 To obtain a chromatogram with a mass spectrometer detector the ion currents for all of the ions (or sometimes selected ions) from the sample are summed and plotted as a function time to give the chromatogram. In GC/IR, the chromatogram is usually obtained with a nondestructive detector, such as a thermal conductivity detector. The output from this detector then triggers the infrared scan for identifying each component that has exited from the column.

27-19 The partition coefficient for a polar compound will be larger on the carbowax 20M column than on the nonpolar SE-30 column.

27-20

Sample	Adjusted Retention Time, t_r'	Retention Index, I
n-Pentane	1.59	500
n-Hexane	3.66	600
1-Hexene	2.58	

For 1-hexene

$$I = 500 + \frac{(\log 2.58 - \log 1.59)}{(\log 3.66 - \log 1.59)} \times 100 = \underline{558}$$

27-21 (a) $p_{H_2O} = 18$ torr at 21.1°C

Substituting into Equation 27-3 (page 702)

$$F = 24.3 \times \frac{375}{294.1} \times \frac{(748 - 18.8)}{748} = \underline{30.2 \text{ mL/min}}$$

$$V_M^0 = jt_M F \times t_M F$$

$$P_i = 748 \text{ torr} + 23.1 \text{ psi} \times 5.17 \text{ torr/psi} = 867 \text{ torr}$$

$$j = \frac{3[(867/748)^2 - 1]}{2[(867/748)^3 - 1]} = 0.925 \quad \text{(Equation } 27-5\text{)}$$

(b) $V_M^0 = jt_M F = 0.925 (18.0/60.0) \times 30.2 = \underline{8.4 \text{ mL}}$

$$(V_R^0)_1 = 0.925 \times 1.98 \times 3.02 = \underline{55.3 \text{ mL}}$$

$$(V_R^0)_2 = 0.925 \times 4.16 \times 30.2 = \underline{116.2 \text{ mL}}$$

$$(V_R^0)_3 = 0.925 \times 7.93 \times 30.2 = \underline{221.5 \text{ mL}}$$

(c) Substituting into Equation 27-6 (page 702) gives

$$(V_g)_1 = \frac{55.3 - 8.38}{1.40} \times \frac{273}{375} = (55.3 - 8.4) \times 0.520 = \underline{24.4 \text{ mL/g stationary phase}}$$

$$(V_g)_2 = (116.2 - 8.4) \times 0.520 = \underline{56.1 \text{ mL/g}}$$

$$(V_g)_3 = (221.5 - 8.4) \times 0.520 = \underline{111 \text{ mL/g}}$$

(d) We rearrange Equation 27-7 to give $K = V_g \rho_S T_c / 273$

$$K_1 = 24.4 \times 1.02 \times 375/273 = 24.4 \times 1.40 = \underline{34.2}$$

$$K_2 = 56.1 \times 0.668 = \underline{78.6}$$

$$K_3 = 111 \times 0.668 = \underline{156}$$

(e)

	t_r, min	t_r'	$\log t_r'$	# C atoms
Air	18/60 = 0.30			
Methyl acetate	1.98	1.68	0.225	3
Methyl propionate	4.16	3.86	0.587	4
Methyl butyrate	7.93	7.63	0.883	5

A plot of $\log t_r'$ versus the # C atoms yields a straight line. From a least-squares analysis, the equation for the line is

$$\log t_r' \;=\; m\,(\text{\# C atoms}) + b \;=\; 0.329\,(\text{\# C atoms}) - 0.75$$

For 7 C atoms

$$\log t_r' \;=\; 0.329 \times 7 - 0.75 \;=\; 1.55$$

$$t_r' \;=\; 35.72 \quad \text{and} \quad t_r \;=\; 35.72 + 0.3 \;=\; \underline{\underline{36.03 \text{ min}}}$$

$$V_R^0 \;=\; j t_M F \;=\; 0.925 \times 36.03 \times 30.2 \;=\; \underline{\underline{1.01 \times 10^3 \text{ mL}}}$$

27-22 (a) $k_1' \;=\; (1.98 - 18.0/60)/(18/60) \;=\; (1.98 - 0.30)/0.30 \;=\; 5.60 \;=\; \underline{\underline{5.6}}$

$k_2' \;=\; (4.16 - 0.30)/0.30 \;=\; 12.9 \;=\; \underline{\underline{13}}$

$k_3' \;=\; (7.93 - 0.30)/0.30 \;=\; 25.4 \;=\; \underline{\underline{25}}$

(b) $\alpha_{2,1} \;=\; 12.9/5.60 \;=\; 2.30 \;=\; \underline{\underline{2.3}}$

$\alpha_{3,2} \;=\; 25.4/12.9 \;=\; 1.98 = \underline{\underline{2.0}}$

(c) $N \;=\; 16\,(t_R/W)^2$

$N_1 \;=\; 16\,(1.98/0.19)^2 \;=\; 1738$

$N_2 \;=\; 16\,(4.16/0.39)^2 \;=\; 1820$

$N_3 \;=\; 16\,(7.93/0.79)^2 \;=\; 1612$

$\overline{N} \;=\; 5170/3 \;=\; 1723 \;=\; \underline{\underline{1.7 \times 10^3}}$

$H \;=\; 110 \text{ cm}/1723 \text{ plates} \;=\; \underline{\underline{0.064 \text{ cm}/\text{plates}}}$

(d) $(R_s)_{2,1} \;=\; 2\,(4.16 - 1.98)/(0.39 + 0.19) \;=\; \underline{\underline{7.5}}$

$(R_s)_{3,2} \;=\; 1\,(7.93 - 4.16)/(0.79 + 0.39) \;=\; \underline{\underline{6.4}}$

27-23 The retention time would be smaller since the three compounds are relatively polar and would thus be less compatible with a nonpolar solvent.

27-24 Proceeding as in the solution to Problem 27-21e, we write

	# C atoms	t_r'	$\log t_r'$
Ethyl alcohol	2	0.69	- 0.161
n-Propyl alcohol	3	1.51	0.179
n-Butyl alcohol	4	3.57	0.553

A plot the data is linear. The equation for the straight line from a least-squares analysis is

$$\log t_r' = 0.357 \,(\# \, C \text{ atoms}) - 0.881$$

For n-pentyl alcohol

$$\log t_r' = 0.357 \times 5 - 0.88 = 0.903 \quad \text{and} \quad \underline{\underline{t_r' = 8.00}}$$

In the same way, for n-hexyl alcohol

$$\log t_r = 1.262 \quad \text{and} \quad \underline{\underline{t_r' = 18.2}}$$

27-25 (a) Increasing V_S/V_M leads to an increase in the film thickness d_f. This increase causes a marked increase in $c_S \mu$ (see Table 26-3, page 685) and thus H.

(b) Reducing the rate of sample injection will lead to band broadening because all of the molecules do not start down the column at the same instant; reduced efficiency and an increase in H results.

(c) Increasing the injection port temperature will tend to decrease H because the sample evaporation rate will increase. Thus, the sample will be put on the column in a narrow band with less zone spreading.

(d) Increasing the flow rate may cause either increases or decreases in H depending upon the flow rate (see Figure 26-7, page 684).

(e) Reducing particle size increases the surface area and thus decreases film thickness d_f in the $c_S \mu$ term in Equation 26-19 (Table 26-3). A decrease in particle size also makes the $c_M \mu$ term smaller. Both effects then lead to a smaller plate height.

(f) The diffusion rates D_M and D_S increase with temperature. In Table 26-3, it is seen that the $c_S \mu$ and $c_M \mu$ terms become smaller as a consequence while the B/μ term becomes larger. In most cases, an increase in plate height accompanies temperature decreases.

27-26 For normal paraffins, the retention index is the number of carbon atoms in the compound multiplied by 100. Thus,

(a) 300 (b) 400 (c) 500 (d) 600 (e) 700 (f) 800

(g) $(t_R - t_M)$ for toluene lies between *n*-heptane and *n*-octane. Thus for

octane, $\log (t_R - t_M) = \log 25.11 = 1.400$

heptane, $\log (t_R - t_M) = \log 14.08 = 1.149$

toluene, $\log (t_R - t_M) = \log 16.32 = 1.213$

$$I = 700 + 100\left(\frac{1.213 - 1.149}{14.00 - 1.149}\right) = \underline{\underline{726}}$$

(h)
$$I = 400 + 100\left(\frac{\log 2.67 - \log 2.21}{\log 4.10 - \log 2.21}\right) = \underline{\underline{431}}$$

(i)
$$I = 300 + 100\left(\frac{\log 7.60 - \log 1.29}{\log 2.21 - \log 1.29}\right) = \underline{\underline{629}}$$

(j)
$$I = 300 + 100\left(\frac{\log 8.40 - \log 7.61}{\log 14.08 - \log 7.61}\right) = \underline{\underline{616}}$$

(k)
$$I = 500 + 100\left(\frac{\log 6.94 - \log 4.10}{\log 7.61 - \log 4.10}\right) = \underline{\underline{585}}$$

(l)
$$I = 600 + 100\left(\frac{\log 9.83 - \log 7.61}{\log 14.08 - \log 7.61}\right) = \underline{\underline{642}}$$

CHAPTER 28

28-1 (a) Substances that are somewhat volatile and are thermally stable.

(b) Molecular species that are nonvolatile or thermally unstable.

(c) Most low to moderate molecular weight organic compounds that are nonvolatile or thermally unstable.

(d) Substances that are ionic.

(e) High-molecular-weight compounds that are soluble in nonpolar solvents.

(f) High-molecular-weight hydrophilic compounds.

(g) Low-molecular-weight nonpolar gases.

(h) Nonpolar low to moderate molecular weight organic compounds and particularly isomeric organic species.

(i) Small organic and inorganic ions.

28-2 Three methods for improving resolution include:

(1) adjustment of k'_A and k'_B by employing a multicomponent mobile phase and varying the ratio of the components to find an optimal mixture;

(2) variation in the chemical composition of the solvent system in such a way as to make α larger;

(3) employing a different packing in which α is greater.

28-3 In partition chromatography, k' is conveniently varied by using a two (or more) component solvent system and varying the ratio of the solvents.

28-4 In gas-liquid chromatography, α is generally varied by varying the column packing. For liquid chromatography, both column packing and chemical composition of the mobile phase can be varied to yield better α values.

28-5 In adsorption chromatography on an alumina packing, it is generally best to increase the polarity of the mobile phase as the elution proceeds. Thus, the ratio of acetone to benzene should be increased as elution proceeds.

28-6 (a) *Sparging* is a process for removing dissolved gases from a solution by sweeping it with a stream of fine bubbles of an inert gas of low solubility.

(b) In an *isocratic elution*, the solvent composition is held constant throughout the elution.

(c) In a *gradient elution*, two or more solvents are employed and the composition of the eluent is changed continuously or in steps as the separation proceeds.

(d) In a *stop-flow injection*, the flow of solvent is stopped, a fitting at the head of the column is removed, and the sample is injected directly onto the head of the column. The fitting is then replaced and pumping is resumed.

(e) A pellicular packing is made up of small nonporous glass or plastic beads that are coated with a thin layer of a porous material that supports the stationary phase or serves as the stationary phase.

(f) Extra-column broadening is a type of band broadening that occurs as the mobile phase flows through open tubing in HPLC systems. It arises because the flow rate adjacent to the walls of open tubing is slower than the rate in the center of the tube.

(g) A *reversed-phase packing* is a nonpolar packing that is used in partition chromatography with a relatively polar mobile phase.

(h) In a *normal-phase packing*, the stationary phase is quite polar and the mobile phase is relatively nonpolar.

(i) A bulk property detector responds to some property of the mobile phase (such as thermal or electrical conductivity) that is altered by the presence of analytes.

(j) A solute property detector responds to some property of analytes, such as absorbance or fluorescent intensity.

28-7 The linear response range of a detector is the range of analyte concentration or mass over which the detector responds linearly.

28-8 A guard column is a short column through which the mobile phase flows before it reaches the injection port and the analytical column in HPLC equipment. The composition of the guard column is similar to that of the analytical column except that the particles are generally larger to minimize pressure drop. The purpose of the guard column is to remove particulate matter and contaminants from the mobile phase and to saturate the mobile phase with the stationary phase so that losses of that phase from the analytical column are minimized.

28-9 Normal phase partition chromatography and adsorption chromatography are similar in the respect that the stationary phases in both are polar, whereas the mobile phases are relatively nonpolar.

28-10 The ideal HPLC detector is highly sensitive, stable, nondestructive, and reproducible in response over a large concentration or mass range. It has a short response time and exhibits a similar response to all analytes or a selective response to one or more classes of analytes.

28-11 In one type of interface between an HPLC column and a mass spectrometer, the column effluent is split in such a way that a minuscule fraction is fed directly into the ionization chamber. Another interface consists of a moving belt or wire that passes through a heater that removes most of the mobile phase. The belt then carries the analyte residues into the ionization compartment. In the thermospray interface, the mobile phase containing a salt such as ammonium acetate is converted to an aerosol jet in a heated stainless capillary tube where ionization occurs.

28-12 The mobile phase in gas chromatography is an inert gas that has no influence on the distribution of analyte molecules between the mobile and stationary phases. Usually altering the mobile phase has little or no effect on a GLC separation. In liquid chromatography, in contrast, the character of the mobile phase often has a profound effect on the success or failure of the separation. As a consequence, the choice of mobile phase becomes an important variable that can be used to alter k' and α.

28-13 For a normal-phase packing, Equation 28-3 (page 742) applies. That is,

$$\frac{k_2'}{k_1'} = 10^{(P_1' - P_2')/2} \qquad (1)$$

where P_1' and P_2' and P_2' are the polarity indexes of chloroform and cyclohexane, respectively.

(a) $k_1' = (29.1 - 1.05)/1.05 = \underline{\underline{26.7}}$ (Equation 26 – 8)

(b) $P_{AB}' = 0.50 \times 4.1 + 0.50 \times 0.1 = 2.10$ (Equation 28 – 2)

Substituting into (1) gives

$$\frac{10}{26.7} = 10^{(2.1 - P_2')/2}$$

Taking the log of both sides of this equation gives

$$\log\frac{10}{26.7} = -0.427 = (2.1 - P_2')/2$$

$$P_2' = 2 \times 0.427 + 2.1 = 2.95$$

Substituting P_2' for P_{AB}' in Equation 28-2 gives

$$2.95 = \phi_A \times 4.1 + \phi_B \times 0.1$$

and $\phi_A + \phi_B = 1.00$

$$2.95 = 4.1\,\phi_A + 0.1 - 0.1\,\phi_A$$

$$\phi_A = (2.95 - 0.1)/4.0 = 0.712$$

Thus the mixture should be 71% $CHCl_3$ and 29% n-hexane.

28-14 A possible strategy would be to increase or decrease the polarity of the mobile phase by substituting one of the solvents shown in Table 28-2 for chloroform. For example, ethyl acetate or dioxane could be used to obtain a more polar mixture; isopropyl ether or carbon tetrachloride should give a less polar system.

28-15 (a) Adsorption

    (b) Partition

    (c) Ion-exchange

    (d) Normal-phase partition

    (e) Exclusion

28-16 A suppressor column is employed in ion chromatography to reduce the ion concentration of the column eluent that arises from the high concentration of ions required to elute analyte ions from the ion-exchange packing. The suppressor column, which is located between the analytical column and the detector, is packed with an ion-exchange resin that effectively converts the eluent ions to molecular species that have no effect on the conductivity detector.

28-17 Chloroform because it has a higher strength than toluene.

28-18 Solutes will be eluted in increasing order of polarity.

    (a) (1) n-Hexane; (2) benzene; (3) hexanol

    (b) (1) Diethyl ether; (2) ethyl acetate; (3) nitromethane

28-19 Solutes will be eluted in decreasing order of polarity

    (a) (1) Hexanol; (2) benzene; (3) n-hexane

(b) (1) Nitromethane; (2) ethyl acetate; (e) diethyl ether

28-20 $K = (V_2 - V_0)/V_t$ (Equation 28 – 11)

From Figure 28-26,

$$(V_e)_B = 8.6 \text{ units} \quad \text{and} \quad (V_e)_C = 11.7 \text{ units}$$

$$K_B = (8.6 - 5.1)/(14.2 - 5.1) = 0.384 = \underline{0.38}$$

$$K_C = (11.7 - 5.1)/(14.2 - 5.1) = 0.726 = \underline{0.73}$$

28-21 A mass chromatogram is a plot of total ion current or ion current for one or more ions in a mass spectrogram as a function of chromatographic retention time. It is obtained by passing the eluent from a chromatographic column into a mass spectrometer and measuring the total ion current or the ion current when the spectrometer is set to one or more m/z ratios.

28-22 For an optimal separation,

$$R_{SO} = \frac{2(t_B - t_A)}{W_{AO} + W_{BO}}$$

For a larger sample volume V_S, assuming retention times do not vary

$$R_S = \frac{2(t_B - t_A)}{W_A + W_B}$$

Combining the two equations to obtain the relative change in resolution

$$\frac{R_{SO} - R_S}{R_{SO}} = 1 - \frac{R_S}{R_{SO}} = 1 - \frac{2(t_B - t_A)/(W_A + W_B)}{2(t_B - t_A)/(W_{AO} + W_{BO})} = 1 - \frac{W_{AO} + V_{BO}}{W_A + W_B}$$

$$W_{AO} + W_{BO} = 9 \text{ s} + 9 \text{ s} = 18 \text{ s}$$

(a)
$$0.05 = 1 - \frac{18 \text{ s}}{W_A + W_B}$$

$$W_A + W_B = \frac{18 \text{ s}}{0.95} = 18.9 \text{ s}$$

At a minimum the volume of sample is the flow rate $F = 2.5$ mL/min times the time $W_A + W_B$, so the maximum volume to achieve the stated change in resolution is then

$$V_S = F(W_A + W_B) = (2.5 \text{ mL/min})(1 \text{ min}/60 \text{ s})(18.9 \text{ s})$$

$$= 0.789 \text{ mL} = \underline{789 \text{ μL}}$$

(b) In the same way, for $\Delta R / R_s = 20\%$, we obtain

$$W_A + W_B = \underline{\underline{22.5 \text{ s}}} \quad \text{and} \quad V_s = \underline{\underline{937 \text{ μL}}}$$

CHAPTER 29

29-1 (a) The critical temperature of a substance is the temperature above which it cannot exist as a liquid phase regardless of pressure. The critical pressure of a substance is the vapor pressure of that substance when it is at its critical temperature.

(b) A supercritical fluid is a substance that is maintained above its critical temperature so that it cannot be liquified regardless of pressure.

29-2 The properties of a super critical fluid that are of particular importance to its application to chromatography are its density, its viscosity, and the rates at which solutes diffuse in it. The magnitude of each of these properties lies intermediate between a typical gas and a typical liquid.

29-3 (a) Instruments for HPLC and SFC are similar except that a column thermostat and a restrictor device are required for SFC and not for HPLC.

(b) SFC instruments are more complex than GLC instruments in that they require a high-pressure pump, a solvent-manifold system, a mobile-phase treatment system, a back-pressure regulator, and often a pulse-damper system.

29-4 Pressure increases cause the density of a super critical fluid to increase which causes the k' for analytes to change. Generally increases in pressure reduce the elution times of solutes.

29-5 Supercritical carbon dioxide has a number of advantages over the liquid phases used in HPLC including: low cost, nontoxicity, ready availability, lack of odor, and its relatively high critical temperature and low critical pressure.

29-6 Supercritical fluid chromatography is ordinarily faster than HPLC and exhibits less band spreading than is encountered in GLC. In contrast to GLC, SFC separations can be carried out at relatively low temperatures thus making the technique applicable to thermally unstable and nonvolatile species. Unlike HPLC, but like GLC, flame ionization can be used for detection, which makes the method applicable to more analytes.

29-7 (a) Initially, an increase in flow rate will shorten the elution time to a minimum value, after which the elution time will increase almost linearly with flow rate (see Figure 29-3).

(b) Pressure increases result in reduction in elution times.

(c) Temperature increases result in a reduction in elution times

CHAPTER 30

30-1 Electroosmotic flow occurs when a mobile phase in a chromatographic column is subjected to a high potential difference between one end of the tube and the other. For a silica tube, the flow is generally away from the positive electrode towards the negative. The flow occurs because of the attraction of positive charged species toward the negative silica surface. This ring of positive charge is mobile and is attracted toward the negative electrode carrying with it the mobile phase molecules.

30-2 Electroosmotic flow can be repressed by reducing the charge on the interior of the capillary by chemical treatment of the surface.

30-3 In solution, amino acids exist as zwitterions that bear both a positive and a negative charge. At low pH values, the net effective charge is positive owing to the interaction of hydrogen ions with the amine groups of the amino acid, whereas at high pH values the net charge is negative due to the dissociation of the carboxylic acid groups. Thus, at low pH values the protein molecules will be strongly attracted toward the negative electrode, while in basic solutions the reverse will be the case.

30-4 Under the influence of an electrical field mobile ions in a solution are attracted or repelled by the negative potential of one of the electrodes. The rate of movement toward or away from a negative electrode is dependent upon the net charge on the analyte and the size and shape of the analyte molecules. These properties vary from analyte to analyte. Thus the rate at which molecules migrate under the influence of the electrical field vary, and the time it takes them to traverse the column varies, thus making separations possible.

30-5 Micellar electrokinetic capillary chromatography serves to separate neutral species under the influence of a high potential difference. In this technique, neutral analyte molecules are solubilitized in micelles that usually bear a negative charge owing to the presence of sulfonic acid anions on their surface. This charge repels the micelles from the negative electrode. Normally, however, this repulsion is more than offset by the osmotic flow. Thus, the micelles move toward the negative electrode at a rate that is less than that of the mobile phase. As a consequence, the micelles act like a slowly moving stationary phase. Separations then occur in the same way as on an HPLC column.

30-6 The advantages of micellar electrokinetic capillary chromatography over HPLC are higher column efficiencies and the ease with which the pseudostationary phase can be altered.

CHAPTER 31

31-1 (a) In thermogravimetric analysis, the mass of a sample is measured as a function of temperature.

(b) In differential thermal analysis, the difference in temperature between the sample and an inert reference is measured as a function of temperature.

(c) In differential scanning calorimetry, the difference in heat needed to keep the sample and reference at the same temperature is recorded as a function of temperature. During an endothermic transition, energy must be supplied to the sample, and during an exothermic transition energy is added to the reference.

(d) In isothermal differential scanning calorimetry, the sample and reference are maintained at the same temperature while this temperature is increased or decreased (usually linearly). The thermal energy required to maintain isothermal conditions is monitored as a function of temperature.

31-2 wt CaC_2O_4 + wt BaC_2O_4 = 0.5713

wt $CaCO_3$ + wt $BaCO_3$ = 0.4673

$$\text{wt } CaC_2O_4 = \frac{\text{wt Ca} \times \text{gfw } CaC_2O_4}{\text{gfw Ca}} = \frac{\text{wt Ca} \times 128.1}{40.08} = 3.196 \text{ wt Ca}$$

Similarly,

$$\text{wt } BaC_2O_4 = \text{wt Ba} \times \frac{225.4}{137.3} = 1.642 \text{ wt Ba}$$

$$\text{wt } CaCO_3 = \text{wt Ca} \times \frac{100.00}{40.08} = 2.497 \text{ wt Ca}$$

$$\text{wt } BaCO_3 = \text{wt Ba} \times \frac{197.4}{137.3} = 1.438 \text{ wt Ba}$$

3.196 wt Ca + 1.642 wt Ba = 0.5713

2.497 wt Ca + 1.438 wt Ba = 0.4673

wt Ca = 1.09 g   and   wt Ba = 0.135 g

% Ca = 0.109 × 100/0.6025 = 18.1

% Ba = 0.135 × 100/0.6025 = 22.4

31-3 If 25.0 mg of $FeCl_3 \cdot 6H_2O$ decomposes 19.2 mg of $FeCl_3 \cdot 5/H_2O$ will be the first reaction product, and further heating will produce 15.0 mg of anhydrous $FeCl_3$. There is no change in mass associated with the melting of $FeCl_3$. See the following sketch.

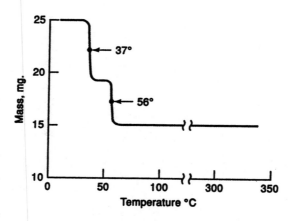

31-4 The melting point of benzoic acid is not very pressure dependent. The boiling point, however, increases as the pressure increases.

31-5 The organic matter in most oil shale is a complex bituminous material called Kerogen that can be converted into recoverable oil. High quality oil shales typically contain 10% to 15% organic matter. A thermogravimetric analysis (TGA) performed in an inert atmosphere would provide an indication of the volatile mass fraction in the sample, and a TGA run in an oxygen atmosphere could be used to evaluate the combustible mass fraction. A DSC experiment run in an inert atmosphere would provide information about the temperature requirements for volatilizing the organic matter, and a DSC run in an oxygen atmosphere would provide information about the total energy content of the sample. (NOTE: Crushing and grinding shale without significantly changing the composition of the sample would be a very challenging part of any such experiment as would obtaining a sample that is representative of an oil shale deposit.)

31-6 The thermocouple is seldom immersed directly in the sample because, first, the precision of the experiment is highly dependent upon the reproducible placement of the thermocouple, and second, the thermocouple may react with the sample or catalyze reactions of the sample.

31-7

Physical Change	Thermal Behavior
Melting / Crystallization	Endo / Exo
Vaporization	Endo
Sublimation	Endo
Adsorption / Desorption	Exo / Endo

31-8

Physical Change	Thermal Behavior
Dehydration	Endo
Decomposition	Endo or Exo
Oxidation	Exo

31-9 DSC and DTA are of more widespread utility than TGA because many important thermal transitions (that is, melting, crystallization, glass transition) are not accompanied by a change in mass.

31-10 The glass-like state of a sample has one heat capacity, and the rubber-like state of the same sample has a different heat capacity. Because the heat capacities for the two states differ there is a shift in the baseline at the glass transition, but (in an ideal sample) no exothermic or endothermic peak is observed.

31-11 Power compensated DSC uses two small individual heaters and temperature sensors (see Figure 31-13), and the power required to keep the sample and reference at the same temperature is the analytical parameter. Heat flux DSC uses a single oven with sample and reference temperature sensors (see Figure 31-14); the difference in the temperature of the sample and reference is proportional to the differential heat flow and serves as the analytical parameter.

CHAPTER 32

32-1 (a) α, or $_2^4He$

(b) β^+

(c) β^-

(d) $^{160}_{62}\text{Sm}$

(e) n

(f) e^- (K capture)

32-2 Substituting into Equation 32-5 (page 813) gives

$$\lambda = \ln 2/t_{1/2} = 0.693/12.36 = 5.61 \times 10^{-2}\,\text{hr}^{-1}$$

Substituting into Equation 32-3 gives

(a) $\ln N/N_0 = -5.61 \times 10^{-2}\,\text{hr}^{-1} \times 1.00\,\text{hr}$

$\quad N/N_0 = \underline{0.945}$

(b) $\ln N/N_0 = -5.61 \times 10^{-2} \times 10.0 = -0.561$

$\quad N/N_0 = \underline{0.571}$

(c) $\ln N/N_0 = -5.61 \times 10^{-2} \times 20.0 = -1.122$

$\quad N/N_0 = \underline{0.326}$

(d) $\ln N/N_0 = -5.61 \times 10^{-2} \times 75.0 = -4.21$

$\quad N/N_0 = \underline{0.0149}$

32-3 (a) Substituting into Equation 32-5 gives

$$\lambda = \frac{0.693}{44.51\,\text{days}} \times \frac{1\,\text{day}}{24\,\text{hr}} = 6.49 \times 10^{-4}\,\text{hr}^{-1}$$

Substituting into Equation 32-3 gives

$$\ln(N/N_0) = -6.49 \times 10^{-4}\,\text{hr}^{-1} \times 27\,\text{hr} = -1.752 \times 10^{-2}$$

$$N/N_0 = \underline{0.983}$$

Proceeding in the same way, we obtain

(b) $\lambda = 0.693/3.078 = -0.2251\,\text{hr}^{-1}$

$\quad \ln(N/N_0) = -0.2251 \times 27 = -6079$

$\quad N/N_0 = 2.29 \times 10^{-3}$

(c) $\lambda = \frac{0.693}{4.536\,\text{day}} = \frac{1\,\text{day}}{24\,\text{hr}} = 6.37 \times 10^{-3}\,\text{hr}^{-1}$

$$\ln(N/N_0) \quad = \quad -6.37 \times 10^{-3} \times 27 \quad = \quad 1.719 \times 10^{-1}$$

$$N/N_0 \quad = \quad \underline{0.842}$$

(d)
$$\lambda \quad = \quad \frac{0.692}{25.3 \text{ day}} \times \frac{1 \text{ day}}{24 \text{ hr}} \quad = \quad 1.1413 \times 10^{-3} \text{ hr}^{-1}$$

$$\ln N/N_0 \quad = \quad -1.1413 \times 10^{-3} \text{ hr}^{-1} \times 27 \text{ hr} \quad = \quad -3.0815 \times 10^{-2}$$

$$N/N_0 \quad = \quad 0.970$$

32-4 $\quad \lambda \quad = \quad 0.693/21.5 \text{ hr} \quad = \quad 3.223 \times 10^{-2} \text{ hr}^{-1}$

$$\ln N/N_0 \quad = \quad \ln(0.0100/1.00) \quad = \quad -3.223 \times 10^{-2} \text{ hr}^{-1} \, t \text{ (hr)}$$

$$= \quad -4.605 \quad = \quad -3.223 \times 10^{-2} t$$

$$t \quad = \quad \underline{143 \text{ hr} \quad \text{or} \quad 5.95 \text{ days}}$$

32-5 $\quad \sigma_M = \sqrt{M} \quad$ and $\quad (\sigma_M)_r = 1/\sqrt{M} \quad$ (Equations $32-10$ and $32-11$, page000)

(a) $\quad \sigma_M = \sqrt{100.0} = \underline{10.0 \text{ counts}} \quad$ and $\quad (\sigma_M)_r = 1/\sqrt{100} = 0.100 \quad$ or $\quad \underline{10.0\%}$

Similarly,

(b) $\quad \sigma = \sqrt{750} = \underline{27.4 \text{ counts}} \quad$ and $\quad (\sigma_M)_r = 100/\sqrt{750} = \underline{3.65\%}$

(c) $\quad \sigma_M = \sqrt{7000} = \underline{83.7 \text{ counts}} \quad$ and $\quad (\sigma_M)_r = 100/\sqrt{7000} = \underline{1.20\%}$

(d) $\quad \sigma_M = \sqrt{2.00 \times 10^4} = \underline{141 \text{ counts}} \quad$ and $\quad (\sigma_M)_r = 100/\sqrt{2.00 \times 10^4} = \underline{7.70\%}$

32-6 Employing Equations 32-10 and 32-11, we write

$$\sigma_M = \sqrt{800} = 28.3 \text{ counts} \quad \text{and} \quad (\sigma_M)_r = 1/\sqrt{800} = 0.0354 \quad \text{or} \quad 3.54\%$$

(a) 50% CL $= 800 \pm z \sigma_M$

From Table a1-3, page A-11, we find $z = 0.67$ and

$$50\% \text{ CL} \quad = \quad 800 \, (\pm 0.67 \times 28.3 \text{ counts}) \quad = \quad \underline{800 \, (\pm 19) \text{ counts}}$$

In relative terms

$$50\% \text{ CL} \quad = \quad 800 \, (\pm 0.67 \times 3.54\%) \quad = \quad \underline{800 \, (\pm 2.4\%)}$$

(b) 90% CL $\quad=\quad 800\,(\pm\,1.64\times28.3\text{ counts})\quad=\quad \underline{\underline{800\,(\pm\,46\text{ counts})}}$

$\qquad\qquad\qquad=\quad 800\,(\pm\,1.64\times3.54\%)\quad=\quad \underline{\underline{800\,(\pm\,5.8\%)}}$

(c) 99% CL $\quad=\quad 800\,(\pm\,2.58\times28.5\text{ counts})\quad=\quad \underline{\underline{800\,(\pm\,73\text{ counts})}}$

$\qquad\qquad\qquad=\quad 800\,(\pm\,2.58\times3.54\%)\quad=\quad \underline{\underline{800\,(\pm\,9.1\%)}}$

32-7 (a) $R_c \quad=\quad R_x - R_b \qquad$ (Equation $32-15$, page 817)

$\qquad\qquad=\quad 300\text{ cpm} - 9\text{ cpm}\quad=\quad \underline{\underline{291\text{ cpm}}}$

(b)
$$\sigma_{R_c}\quad=\quad\sqrt{\frac{R_x}{t_x}+\frac{R_b}{t_b}}\qquad\text{(Equation }32-16,\text{ page 817)}$$

$$=\quad\sqrt{\frac{300\text{ cpm}}{14\text{ min}}+\frac{9\text{ cpm}}{2\text{ min}}}\quad=\quad \underline{\underline{5.09\text{ cpm}}}$$

(c) 90% CL for $R_c \quad=\quad R_c \pm z\,\sigma_{R_c}\qquad$ (Equation $32-14$, page 916)

$\qquad\qquad\qquad=\quad 291\text{ cpm}\pm1.64\,(5.09\text{ cpm})\quad=\quad \underline{\underline{291\pm8\text{ cpm}}}$

32-8
$$\sigma_{R_c}\quad=\quad\sqrt{\frac{R_x}{t_x}+\frac{R_b}{t_b}}\qquad\text{(Equation }32-16,\text{ page 817)}$$

$$\left(\sigma_{R_c}\right)_r\quad=\quad\sqrt{\frac{\frac{R_x}{t_x}+\frac{R_b}{t_b}}{R_x - R_b}}$$

(a)
$$0.05\quad=\quad\frac{\sqrt{\frac{90\text{ cpm}}{t_x}+\frac{9\text{ cpm}}{3\text{ min}}}}{90\text{ cpm} - 9\text{ cpm}}$$

$$16.4\text{ cpm}^2\quad=\quad\frac{90\text{ cpm}}{t_x}+3\text{ cpm}^2$$

$$t_x\quad=\quad 6.72\text{ min}$$

$$M\quad=\quad t_x\times R_x\quad=\quad 6.72\text{ min}\times90\text{ cpm}\quad=\quad \underline{\underline{605\text{ counts}}}$$

(b)
$$0.05\quad=\quad\frac{\sqrt{\frac{300\text{ cpm}}{t_x}+\frac{9\text{ cpm}}{3\text{ min}}}}{300\text{ cpm} - 9\text{ cpm}}$$

$$212\text{ cpm}^2\quad=\quad\frac{300\text{ cpm}}{t_x}+3\text{ cpm}^2$$

$$t_x = 1.44 \text{ min}$$

$$M = t_x \times R_x = 1.44 \text{ min} \times 300 \text{ cpm} = \underline{\underline{432 \text{ counts}}}$$

32-9 Equation 32-4 (page 813) can be used to calculate the decay constant λ

$$2230 \text{ cpm} = 3250 \text{ cpm } e^{-\lambda(10.0 \text{ hr})}$$

$$\ln\left(\frac{2230}{3250}\right) = -\lambda(10.0 \text{ hr})$$

$$\lambda = 0.0377 \text{ hr}^{-1}$$

Equation 32-5 can be used to calculate the half-life.

$$t_{1/2} = \frac{\ln 2}{\lambda} = \frac{0.693}{0.0377 \text{ hr}^{-1}} = \underline{\underline{18.4 \text{ hr}}}$$

32-10 Equation 32-5 can be used to calculate the delay constants

$$\lambda\,(^{36}\text{Cl}) = \frac{0.693}{87.2 \text{ min} \times 1 \text{ hr}/60 \text{ min}} = 0.4768 \text{ hr}^{-1}$$

$$\lambda\,(^{35}\text{S}) = \frac{0.693}{37.5 \text{ days} \times 24 \text{ hr}/\text{day}} = 7.70 \times 10^{-4} \text{ hr}^{-1}$$

Equation 23-8 can be written in terms of activity rather than counting rates

$$A\,(^{38}\text{Cl}) = A_0\,(^{38}\text{Cl}) \exp(-0.4768\,t)$$

$$A\,(^{35}\text{S}) = A_0\,(^{35}\text{S}) \exp(-7.70 \times 10^{-4}\,t)$$

or

$$0.001 = \frac{A_0\,(^{38}\text{Cl})}{A_0\,(^{35}\text{S})} = \frac{A_0\,(^{38}\text{Cl}) \exp(-0.468\,t)}{A_0\,(^{35}\text{S}) \exp(-7.70 \times 10^{-4})}$$

But $A_0\,(^{38}\text{Cl}) = A_0\,(^{35}\text{S})$

Therefore

$$0.001 = \exp(-0.468\,t + 7.70 \times 10^{-4}\,t)$$

Taking the ln of each side of this equation gives

$$-0.6908 = -0.468\,t + 7.70 \times 10^{-4}\,t$$

$$t = 1.48 \text{ hr} \quad \text{or} \quad 1.5 \text{ hr}$$

32-11

$$(\sigma_R)_r \; = \; \frac{\sigma_R}{R} \; = \; \frac{\sigma_M / t}{M / t} \; = \; \frac{\sigma_M}{M}$$

Using Equation 32-10 to replace σ_M gives the desired result

$$(\sigma_R)_r \; = \; \frac{\sigma_M}{M} \; = \; \frac{\sqrt{M}}{M} \; = \; M^{-1/2}$$

32-12 (a) Equation 32-17 and Figure 32-6 show that irradiation for approximately one minute will produce near saturation activity for ^{19}F, and that in this time only a negligible amount of ^{42}K would be produced. If a beta detector is to be used for analysis it would be desirable to minimize the number of other data emitting species (^{42}K in this case). Because the activity due to ^{20}F will be decaying rapidly, counting should be started as soon as possible after irradiation.

(b) In this case Equation 32-17 and Figure 32-6 show that irradiation for on the average of two days would be required to approach saturation activity for ^{42}K. To minimize the interference form ^{20}F it would be desirable to insert a long delay between the end of irradiation and the start of counting. For example, 12.4 hr after irradiation the ^{42}K activity would be one half its maximum value, but Equation 32-8 can be used to show that the ^{20}F activity will have decayed to a negligible value.

32-13 Equation 32-17 can be used to calculate activity A,

$$A \; = \; N \phi \sigma S$$

For ^{19}F,

$$N \; = \; 1 \text{ mmol F} \times 6.02 \times 10^{20} \frac{\text{F atom}}{\text{mmol}} \; = \; 6.0 \times 10^{20} \text{ F target atoms}$$

$$\phi \; = \; 1.0 \times 10^{13} \text{ cm}^{-2} \text{ s}^{-2}$$

$$\sigma \; = \; 9.0 \times 10^{-27} \text{ cm}^2 / \text{target atoms}$$

$$S \; = \; 1 - \exp(-0.693 \times 60 \text{ s} \backslash 11 \text{ s}) \; = \; 0.98$$

$$A \; = \; 6.0 \times 10^{20} \times 1.0 \times 10^{13} \times 9.0 \times 10^{-27} \times 0.98 \; = \; \underline{5.3 \times 10^7 \text{ decays/s}}$$

For ^{41}K, since 7% of K is ^{41}K

$$N \; = \; 6.0 \times 10^{20} \times 0.070 \; = \; 4.2 \times 10^{19} \text{ target atoms}$$

$$\phi \; = \; 1.0 \times 10^{13} \text{ cm}^2 \text{ s}^{-1}$$

$$\sigma \; = \; 1.1 \times 10^{-24} \text{ cm}^2 / \text{target atoms}$$

$$S \; = \; 1 - \exp(-0.693 \times 1 \text{ min} / 12.4 \text{ hr} \times 60 \text{ min/hr} \; = \; 9.3 \times 10^{-4}$$

$$A = 4.2 \times 10^{19} \times 1.0 \times 10^{12} \times 1.1 \times 10^{-24} \times 9.3 \times 10^{-4} = \underline{\underline{4.3 \times 10^{5} \text{ decays/s}}}$$

32-14 If the activity of the tracer is large, the weight of the added tracer W_T can be kept small and the second term will be negligible relative to the first and we may write

$$W_X = \frac{R_T W_M}{R_M} - W_T \approx \frac{R_T}{R_M} W_M$$

32-15 We will modify Equation 32-23 letting R_M and R_T be the activities of the sample containing the tracer and the tracer itself respectively and W_M, W_X, and W_T will be the volumes of the isolated sample, the unknown, and the tracer respectively.

$$R_T = 0.120 \frac{\mu \text{Ci}}{\text{mL}} \times 2.00 \text{ mL} \times 3.70 \times 10^{10} \frac{\text{cps}}{\text{Ci}} \times 10^{-6} \frac{\text{Ci}}{\mu \text{Ci}} = 8.8 \times 10^{3} \text{ cps}$$

$$R_M = 15.8 \text{ cps}$$

$$\text{blood volume} = W_X = \frac{R_T}{R_M} W_M - W_T \quad \text{(Equation 32-23)}$$

$$= \frac{8.8 \times 10^{3} \text{ cps}}{15.8 \text{ cps}} \times 1.00 \text{ mL} - 2.00 \text{ mL} = 560 \text{ mL}$$

32-16 $A_0 = 5.42 \times 10^{3} \text{ cpm mg}^{-1} \times 0.981 \text{ mg} = 5.32 \times 10^{3} \text{ cpm}$

Substituting into Equation 32-23

$$W_X = \text{mg penicillin} = \frac{5.32 \times 10^{3} \text{ cpm}}{343 \text{ cpm}} \times 0.406 \text{ mg} - 0.981 \text{ mg} = \underline{\underline{5.32 \text{ mg}}}$$

32-17 We first convert the activity to specific activities in terms of Cl^-.

For NaCl,

$$R_T = \frac{4.0 \times 10^{4} \text{ cps}}{1.0 \text{ mg NaCl} \times 35.5 \text{ mg Cl} / 58.44 \text{ mg NaCl}}$$

$$= 6.58 \times 10^{4} \text{ cps/mg Cl}^-$$

$$R'_M = \frac{35 \text{ cps}}{400 \text{ mg AgCl} \times 35.5 \text{ mg Cl} / 143.3 \text{ mg AgCl}}$$

$$= 0.353 \text{ cps/mg Cl}^-$$

In order to correct R_M for the time delay, we employ Equation 32-5 to obtain λ.

$$\lambda \ = \ 0.693/37.3 \ \text{min} \ = \ 1.86 \times 10^{-2} \ = \ 0.0186 \ \text{min}$$

Equation 32-8 is rearranged to give the counting rate before any decay. Thus,

$$R_M \ = \ 0.353 \ \exp \ (0.0186 \ \text{min} \times 148 \ \text{min}) \ = \ 5.54 \ \text{cps}$$

Substituting into Equation 32-23

$$W_X \ = \ \frac{6.58 \times 10^4 \ \text{cps} / \text{mg Cl}^-}{5.54 \ \text{cps} / \text{mg Cl}^-} \times 3.0 \ \text{mg Cl}^- - 3.0 \ \text{mg Cl}^-$$

$$= \ 3.6 \times 10^4 \ \text{mg Cl}^- \quad \text{or} \quad \underline{36 \ \text{g Cl}^-}$$

32-18 (a) Because ^{14}C has a long half life,

$$W_X \ = \ \frac{1000 \ \text{cpm/mg}}{20 \ \text{cpm/mg}} \times 3.0 - 3.0 \ \text{mg} \qquad \text{(Equation } 32-23)$$

$$\% \ \text{threonine} \ = \ \frac{147 \times 10^{-3} \ \text{g}}{10.0 \ \text{g}} \times 100\% \ = \ \underline{\underline{1.5\%}}$$

(b) Proceeding as in Problem 32-17 to obtain a corrected count

$$\lambda \ = \ 0.693/20.5 \ \text{min} \ = \ 3.38 \times 10^{-2} \ \text{min}^{-1}$$

$$R_M \ = \ 20 \ \frac{\text{cpm}}{\text{mg}} \times \exp \ (3.38 \times 10^{-2} \ \text{min}^{-1} \times 32 \ \text{min}) \ = \ 59.0 \ \text{cpm/mg}$$

Then, proceeding as in part (a), we obtain

$$W_X \ = \ \frac{1000}{59.0} \times 3.0 - 3.0 \ = \ 47.8$$

$$\% \ = \ \frac{47.8 \times 10^{-3}}{10} \times 1000 \ = \ \underline{\underline{0.48\% \ \text{threonine}}}$$

32-19 $A_0 \ = \ 223 \ \text{cpm mg}^{-1} \times 1.34 \ \text{mg} \ = \ 299 \ \text{cpm}$

$$W_X \ = \ \text{mg analyte} \ = \ \frac{299 \ \text{cpm}}{(654/60) \ \text{cpm}} \times 0.112 \ \text{mg} - 1.34 \qquad \text{(Equation } 32-23)$$

$$= \ 1.73$$

$$\text{ppm analyte} \ = \ \frac{1.73 \ \text{mg analyte}}{500 \times 10^3 \ \text{mg sample}} \times 10^6 \ = \ 3.46$$

32-20 The kinetic energy KE of thermal neutrons is given by

$$KE = \frac{3}{2}kT$$

where k is the Boltzmann constannt. Thus, assuming $T = 298$ K,

$$KE = \frac{3}{2}(1.39 \times 10^{-23} \text{ J K}^{-1} \times 298 \text{ K} \times 6.24 \times 10^{18} \text{ eV J}^{-1})$$

$$= 0.039 \approx \underline{\underline{0.04 \text{ eV}}}$$

32-21 (a) We employ Equation 23-17

$$A = N\phi\sigma S$$

If we assume a unit detection coefficient

$$S = 1 - \exp(-0.693\, t/t_{1/2})$$

$$= 1 - \exp(-0.693 \times 1.00 \text{ hr}/2.58 \text{ hr}) = 0.236$$

$$A = 10 \text{ cpm} \times (1 \text{ min}/60 \text{ s}) = 0.167 \text{ s}^{-1}$$

$$\phi = 1.8 \times 10^{12} \text{ cm}^{-2} \text{ s}^{-1}$$

$$\sigma = 13.3 \times 10^{-24} \text{ cm}^2$$

$$N \approx \frac{0.167 \text{ s}^{-1}}{(1.8 \times 10^{12} \text{ cm}^{-2} \text{ s}^{-1})(13.3 \times 10^{-24} \text{ cm}^2)(0.236)} \approx 3.0 \times 10^{10} \text{ atoms}$$

$$3.0 \times 10^{10} \text{ atoms} \times \left(\frac{1 \text{ mol}}{6.02 \times 10^{23} \text{ atoms}}\right)\left(\frac{55 \text{ g Mn}}{\text{mol}}\right) = \underline{\underline{2.7 \times 10^{-12} \text{ g}}} \text{ or } 2.7 \times 10^{-6} \text{ μg}$$

(b) The tabulated value was calculated assuming that a 3 x 3 in. NaI (TL) detector was used. The detection coefficients with such systems depends upon the specific geometry, but typically they are in the 10% to 15% region ($c \approx 0.1$ to 0.15). Thus accounting for most of the difference between the calculated and tabulated values.

CHAPTER 33

33-1 (a) Sample Preparation: grind and mix.

Sample Definition: transfer a small sample to a small blank or test tube.

Sample Dissolution: heat with an aqueous oxidizing acid followed by dilute with water.

Separation: none required.

Measurement: excite ICP spectrum.

Calibration: excite a standard lead solution and compare spectra with that of the unknown.

Data Reduction: if lead present, make rough estimate of the amount by comparing line intensity with standard.

Data Presentation: report presence or absence of lead with rough estimate of the amount if any detected.

(b) Sample Preparation: count out, grind, and homogenize several tablets.

Sample Definition: weigh out replicate samples of the solid into small beakers.

Sample Dissolution: heat the samples in concentrated HCl.

Separation: filter the insoluble residue from the solution.

Sample Definition: dilute to a known volume and introduce aliquots into a suitable container.

Color Development: adjust pH and add a measured volume of KSCN solution.

Photometric Measurement: determine absorbance with a green filter.

Calibration: for several standard iron solutions, add KSCN and prepare an absorbance versus concentration plot.

Data Reduction: calculate the iron concentration and the standard deviation of the data.

Data Presentation: point out the results and the precision of the data.

33-2 Shown below is a flow injection system for determining Na^+ and K^+ in an aqueous sample. After sample injection, the solution is fed directly into a burner fueled by a natural gas mixture. The radiation is directed into two recording photometers with interference filters one of which transmits one of the sodium lines and the other a potassium line.

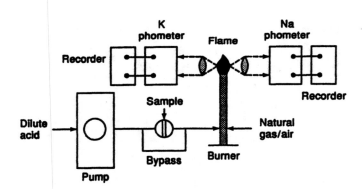

33-3 In the apparatus that follows, the sample is injected into a buffered solvent and transported to a mixing are where it is mixed with CCl_4. The apparatus is similar to that shown in Figure 33-8.

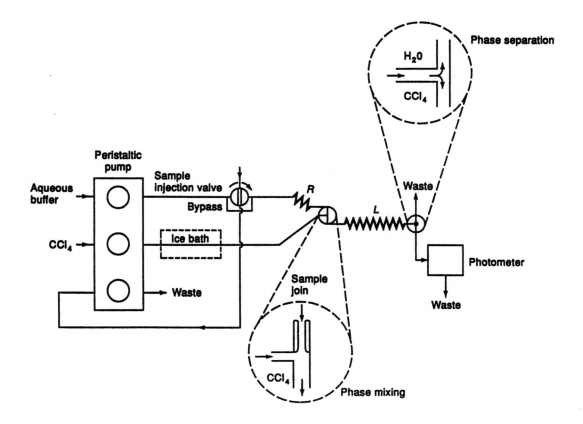

33-4 The apparatus shown below is for the determination of sulfate. The sample is injected into a stream of dilute H_2SO_4, which converts SO_3^{2-} to SO_2. The membrane in this case is porous and transmits part of the SO_2 into the stream containing a colorimetric reagent for SO_2.

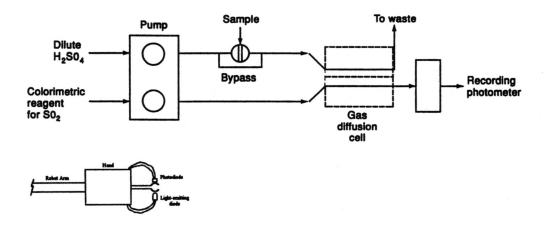

33-5

33-6 The sample is injected, and the solvent separates from the analytes on the relatively short general purpose cleanup column. As soon as the solvent passes through detector 1, the detector generates an electrical signal that switches the solenoid valve from waste to the analytical column where the two analytes are separated. The analyte peaks are then recorded by detector 2, integrated, and the results appear on the readout.

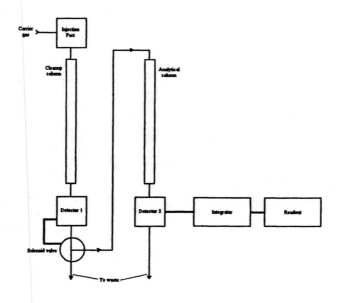

APPENDIX 1

a1-1 For A

x_i	x_i^2
61.45	3776.1025
61.53	3785.9409
61.30	3760.1424
$\sum x_i = 184.32$	$\sum x_i^2 = 11322.1858$

(a) $\bar{x}$ = 184.30/3 = <u>61.43</u>

There are three degrees of freedom because only one result is being derived from the three data.

(b)
$$s = \sqrt{\frac{\sum x_i^2 - (\sum x_i)^2/3}{3-1}} = \sqrt{\frac{11322.1858 - (184.30)^2/3}{2}} \qquad \text{(Equation a1 – 12)}$$

$$= \sqrt{\frac{11322.1858 - 11322.1633}{2}} = \sqrt{\frac{0.0225}{2}}$$

$$= 0.106 = \underline{0.11}$$

Here, there are only two degrees of freedom because the data are used to determine two quantities, $\bar{x}$ and s.

(c) standard error = s_m = $s/\sqrt{N}$ = $0.106\sqrt{3}$ = <u>0.064</u>   (Equation a1 – 17)

(d) $CV = 0.106 \times 100/61.43 = \underline{\underline{0.17\%}}$ (Equation a1 – 11)

The remaining sets are treated in the same way. The results are:

		A	B	C	D
	$\sum x_1$	184.30	19.52	24.200	10.60
	$\sum (x_i)^2$	11322.1858	63.507	292.8232	28.22
(a)	$\bar{x}$	61.43	3.25	12.10	2.64
	df	3	6	2	4
(b)	s	0.11	0.020	0.057	0.21
	df	2	5	1	3
(c)	s_m	0.064	0.0082	0.040	0.10
(d)	CV	0.18%	0.60%	0.47%	7.9%

a1-2 For A

(a) abs error $= \bar{x} - x_t = 61.43 - 61.71 = \underline{\underline{-0.28}}$

(b) abs error $= -0.28 \times 100/61.71 = \underline{\underline{-0.45\%}}$

Proceeding in the same way we obtain

	A	B	C	D
(a)	– 0.28	– 0.030	– 0.13	– 0.10
(b)	– 0.45%	– 0.91%	– 1.1%	– 3.6%

a1-3   (a) rel error $= -0.5 \times 100/25 = \underline{\underline{-2.0\%}}$

(b) rel error $= -0.5 \times 100/100 = \underline{-0.5\%}$

(c) rel error $= -0.5 \times 100/250 = \underline{\underline{-0.2\%}}$

(d) rel error $= -0.5 \times 100/500 = \underline{\underline{-0.1\%}}$

a1-4 (a)

$$\% \, Cu = \frac{wt \, Cu}{wt \, smple} \times 100 = 4.8$$

$$wt \, sample = \frac{wt \, Cu \times 100}{4.8} = 20.8 \, wt \, Cu \quad (1)$$

$$\% \, rel \, error = \frac{0.5 \times 10^{-3} \, g \times 100}{wt \, Cu, \, g}$$

151

$$wt\ Cu\ =\ \frac{0.050}{\%\ rel\ error}\qquad(2)$$

Substituting equation (1) into (2) gives

$$wt\ sample\ =\ \frac{20.8\times0.050}{\%\ rel\ error}\ =\ \frac{1.04}{\%\ rel\ error}\ g$$

Substituting the relative errors into this equation gives

(a) <u>10 g</u>   (b) <u>2.1 g</u>   (c) <u>1.3 g</u>   (d) <u>0.87 g</u>

a1-5 $s_m\ =\ s/\sqrt{N}$ (Equation a1 – 17)

$$0.01\%\ =\ 1\%/\sqrt{N}$$

$$N\ =\ (1/0.01)^2\ =\ \underline{\underline{1\times10^4\ \text{replicate measurements}}}$$

a1-6 $RSD\ =\ 1.84\times10^{-3}\times100/0.500\ =\ 0.368\%$

Applying Equation a1-17

$$0.100\%\ =\ 0.368\%/\sqrt{N}$$

$$N\ =\ (0.368/0.100)^2\ =\ 13.5\quad\text{or}\quad\underline{\underline{14\ \text{measurements}}}$$

a1-7 theoretical wt Cr $=\ 0.400\times18/100\ =\ 0.072$ g

$$\text{relative error}\ =\ -\frac{1.8\ mg\times10^{-3}\ g/mg}{0.072\ g}\times1000\ ppt\ =\ \underline{\underline{-25\ ppt}}$$

a1-8 (a) See Example a1-3 (page A-11)

1. $(0.14)^2+(0.09)^2+(0.06)^2+(0.00)^2+(0.11)^2\ =\ 4.34\times10^{-2}$

$$s\ =\ \sqrt{4.34\times10^{-2}/4}\ =\ \underline{0.10}$$

2. $(0.07)^2+(0.12)^2+(0.10)^2+(0.01)^2\ =\ 2.94\times10^{-2}$

$$s\ =\ \sqrt{2.94\times10^{-2}/3}\ =\ \underline{0.099}$$

3. $(0.13)^2+(0.05)^2+(0.08)^2(0.14)^2+(0.07)^2\ =\ 5.03\times10^{-2}$

$$s\ =\ \sqrt{5.03\times10^{-2}/4}\ =\ \underline{0.11}$$

4. $(0.10)^2+(0.13)^2+(0.07)^2\ =\ 3.18\times10^{-2}$

$$s = \sqrt{3.18 \times 10^{-2}/2} = \underline{\underline{0.13}}$$

5. $(0.07)^2 + (0.10)^2 + (0.11)^2 + (0.03)^2 + (0.14)^2 + (0.05)^2 = 5.00 \times 10^{-2}$

$$s = \sqrt{5.00 \times 10^{-2}/5} = \underline{\underline{0.10}}$$

(b)
$$s_{pooled} = \sqrt{\frac{(4.34 + 2.94 + 5.03 + 3.18 + 5.00) \times 10^{-2}}{5 + 4 + 5 + 3 + 6 - 5}} = \underline{\underline{0.11}}$$

a1-9 For sample 1

x_i	$x_i - \bar{x}$	$(x_i - \bar{x})^2$
1.5	0.17	0.0289
1.2	-0.13	0.0169
1.3	-0.03	0.0009
$\Sigma x_i = 4.0$		$\Sigma(x_i - \bar{x})^2 = 0.0467$

$$\bar{x} = 4.0/3 = 1.33$$

$$s = \sqrt{\frac{(x_i - \bar{x})^2}{3 - 1}} = \sqrt{\frac{0.0467}{2}} = \underline{\underline{0.15}}$$

The remaining results are treated in the same way giving:

Sample No.	N	$\bar{x}$	$(x_i - \bar{x})^2$	$s = \sqrt{\frac{(x_i - \bar{x})^2}{N - 1}}$
1	3	1.33	0.0467	0.15
2	4	2.20	0.0600	0.14
3	4	1.62	0.0875	0.17
4	5	1.44	0.1320	0.18
$\Sigma N = 16$			$\Sigma(x_i - \bar{x})^2 = 0.3262$	

$$s_{pooled} = \sqrt{0.3262/(16 - 4)} = \underline{\underline{0.16 \, \mu g \, Pb/m^3}}$$

a1-10 (a) $\quad s_y^2 = (0.03)^2 + (0.001)^2 + (0.001)^2 = 9.02 \times 10^{-4}$

$$s_y = \sqrt{9.02 \times 10^{-4}} = \underline{\underline{0.030}}$$

$$CV = \frac{0.0030}{0.572} \times 100\% = \underline{\underline{5.2\%}}$$

$$y = \underline{\underline{0.57 \, (\pm 0.03)}}$$

153

(b)
$$\left(\frac{s_y}{y}\right)^2 = \left(\frac{0.3}{67.1}\right)^2 + \left(\frac{0.02 \times 10^{-17}}{1.03 \times 10^{17}}\right)^2 = 3.970 \times 10^{-4}$$

$$\frac{s_y}{y} = 1.99 \times 10^{-2} \qquad CV = 1.99 \times 10^{-2} \times 100\% = \underline{\underline{2.0\%}}$$

$$s_y = (1.99 \times 10^{-2})(6.9113 \times 10^{-16}) = 0.137 \times 10^{-16} = \underline{0.14 \times 10^{-16}}$$

$$y = \underline{\underline{6.9\,(\pm 0.1) \times 10^{-16}}}$$

(c)
$$\left(\frac{s_y}{y}\right)^2 = \left(\frac{1}{243}\right)^2 + \left(\frac{2}{760}\right)^2 + \left(\frac{0.006}{1.006}\right)^2$$

$$= (4.115 \times 10^{-3})^2 + (2.631 \times 10^{-3})^2 + (5.964 \times 10^{-3})^2$$

$$= (1.693 \times 10^{-5}) + (6.925 \times 10^{-6}) + (3.557 \times 10^{-5})$$

$$= 5.943 \times 10^{-5}$$

$$\frac{s_y}{y} = \sqrt{5.943 \times 10^{-5}} = 7.709 \times 10^{-3}$$

$$CV = (7.709 \times 10^{-3}) \times 100\% = \underline{\underline{0.77\%}}$$

$$s_y = (183578.5)(7.709 \times 10^{-3}) = 1.415 \times 10^3 = \underline{\underline{1.4 \times 10^3}}$$

$$y = 1.84 \times (\pm 0.01) \times 10^5$$

(d)
$$s_{num} = (6)^2 + (3)^2 = 45$$

$$s_{num} = \sqrt{45} = 6.71$$

$$s_{demon}^2 = (1)^2 + (8)^2 = 65$$

$$s_{demon} = \sqrt{65} = 8.06$$

$$y = \frac{143 - 64}{1249 + 77} = \frac{79}{1326} = 5.9578 \times 10^{-2}$$

$$\left(\frac{s_y}{y}\right)^2 = \left(\frac{6.71}{79}\right)^2 + \left(\frac{8.06}{1326}\right) = 7.2511 \times 10^{-3}$$

$$\frac{s_y}{y} = 8.515 \times 10^{-2} \qquad CV = (8.515 \times 10^{-2}) \times 100\% = \underline{\underline{8.5\%}}$$

$$s_y = (8.515 \times 10^{-2})(5.9578 \times 10^{-2}) = \underline{\underline{5.073 \times 10^{-3}}}$$

$$y = \underline{\underline{6.0\,(\pm 0.5) \times 10^{-2}}}$$

(e) $\left(\dfrac{s_y}{y}\right)^2 = \left(\dfrac{0.01}{1.97}\right)^2 + \left(\dfrac{3}{243}\right)^2 = 1.782 \times 10^{-4}$

$\quad\quad \dfrac{s_y}{y} = 1.335 \times 10^{-2} \quad CV = (1.335 \times 10^{-2}) \times 100\% = \underline{1.3\%}$

$\quad\quad s_y = (1.335 \times 10^{-2})(8.106996 \times 10^{-3}) = \underline{\underline{1.082 \times 10^{-4}}}$

$\quad\quad y = \underline{\underline{8.1\,(\pm 0.1) \times 10^{-3}}}$

a1-11 (a) $s_y^2 = (0.02 \times 10^{-7})^2 + (0.2 \times 10^{-8})^2 = 8.0 \times 10^{-18}$

$\quad\quad s_y = 2.8 \times 10^{-9} = 0.03 \times 10^{-7}$

$\quad\quad CV = \dfrac{s_y}{y} \times 100\% = \dfrac{2.8 \times 10^{-9}}{-1.374 \times 10^{-7}} \times 100\% = \underline{2\%}$

$\quad\quad y = \underline{\underline{-1.37\,(\pm 0.03) \times 10^{-7}}}$

(b) $s_y^2 = (0.08)^2 + (0.06)^2 + (0.004)^2 = 0.010$

$\quad\quad s_y = \underline{0.10}$

$\quad\quad CV = \dfrac{0.10}{0.780} \times 100\% = \underline{\underline{13\%}}$

$\quad\quad y = \underline{\underline{0.8 \pm 0.1}}$

(c) $\left(\dfrac{s_y}{y}\right)^2 = \left(\dfrac{0.0005}{0.0010}\right)^2 + \left(\dfrac{0.02}{18.10}\right)^2 + \left(\dfrac{1}{200}\right)^2 = 0.25$

$\quad\quad \dfrac{s_y}{y} = 0.50 \quad CV = 0.50 \times 100\% = \underline{\underline{50\%}}$

$\quad\quad s_y = 0.50\,y = (0.50)(3.62) = \underline{1.8}$

$\quad\quad y = \underline{\underline{4 \pm 2}}$

(d) $\dfrac{s_y}{y} = 3\left(\dfrac{0.03}{33.33}\right) = 2.7 \times 10^{-3}$

$\quad\quad CV = (2.7 \times 10^{-3}) \times 100\% = 0.27\% = \underline{0.3\%}$

$\quad\quad s_y = 0.0027\,y = (0.0027)(37025.927) = 99.98 = \underline{100}$

$\quad\quad y = \underline{\underline{3.70\,(\pm 0.01) \times 10^4}}$

(e) $\left(\dfrac{s_y}{y}\right)^2 = \left(\dfrac{0.03\times10^{-14}}{1.73\times10^{-14}}\right)^2 + \left(\dfrac{0.04\times10^{-16}}{1.63\times10^{-16}}\right)^2 = \left(\dfrac{0.03}{1.73}\right)^2 + \left(\dfrac{0.04}{1.63}\right)^2$

$\qquad = (0.0173)^2 + (0.0245)^2 = 9.03\times10^{-2}$

$\dfrac{s_y}{y} = 3.00\times10^{-2} \qquad CV = (3.00\times10^{-2})\times100\% = \underline{\underline{3\%}}$

$s_y = (3.00\times10^{-2})(106.1349693) = 3.189 = \underline{\underline{3}}$

$y = \underline{\underline{106\pm3}}$

a1-12 See Example a1-4, page A-12.

$$s \to \sigma \qquad 99\%\ CL = 0.025 \pm \dfrac{z\,\sigma}{\sqrt{N}} \qquad z = \pm2.58 \qquad (\text{Table a1}-3)$$

(a) $CL = \bar{x} \pm 2.58\times0.025/\sqrt{1} = \underline{\underline{\bar{x} \pm 0.064\text{ ppb Au}}}$

(b) $CL = \bar{x} \pm 2.58\times0.025/\sqrt{3} = \underline{\underline{\bar{x} \pm 0.037\text{ ppb Au}}}$

(c) $CL = \bar{x} \pm 2.58\times0.025/\sqrt{5} = \underline{\underline{\bar{x} \pm 0.029\text{ ppb Au}}}$

a1-13 See Examples a1-4 and a1-5. Employing Table a1-3 and Equation a1-19 yields

(a) $95\%\ CL = \bar{x} \pm 1.96\times0.030/\sqrt{4} = \underline{\underline{\bar{x} \pm 0.029}}$

(b) $\pm1.96\times0.030/\sqrt{N} = \pm0.017\text{ ppm}$

$$N = \left(\dfrac{1.96\times0.0300}{0.017}\right)^2 = 11.9 \quad \text{or} \quad \underline{\underline{12\text{ measurements}}}$$

a1-14 Proceeding as in the solution to Problem a1-13, we obtain

(a) $\underline{\underline{\bar{x} \pm 0.76\text{ ppm CO}}}$ (b) $6.9 = \underline{\underline{7\text{ measurements}}}$

a1-15

x_i	$x_i - \bar{x}$	$(x_i - \bar{x})^2$
1.10	(-0.004)	1.600×10^{-5}
1.08	(-0.016)	25.60×10^{-5}
1.09	(-0.006)	3.60×10^{-5}
1.12	(-0.024)	57.60×10^{-5}
1.09	(-0.006)	3.60×10^{-5}
5 |5.48		$\Sigma(x_i - \bar{x})^2 = 9.20 \times 10^{-4}$

$x = 1.096$

$$s = \sqrt{\frac{9.20 \times 10^{-4}}{5-1}} = 1.52 \times 10^{-2}$$

$$\frac{ts}{\sqrt{5}} = \frac{2.78 \times 1.52 \times 10^{-2}}{\sqrt{5}} = 1.89 \times 10^{-2}$$

$$\bar{x} - \mu = 1.096 - 1.12 = 2.4 \times 10^{-2}$$

Since 2.4×10^{-2} is greater than 1.89×10^{-2}, <u>bias is suggested at the 95% confidence level</u>.

a1-16 (a) $(\bar{x} - \mu)_{actual} = 30.26 - 30.15 = 0.11$

At the 95% confidence level,

$$(\bar{x} - \mu) = \pm z s_{pooled}/\sqrt{N} = \pm(1.96)(0.094)/\sqrt{4} = \pm 0.092 < 0.11$$

<u>Determinate error is indicated at the 95% confidence level</u>.

(b) $(\bar{x} - \mu) = \pm t s_{exp}/\sqrt{N} = \pm(3.18)(0.085)/\sqrt{4} = \pm 0.135 > 0.11$

<u>No determinate error is demonstrated at the 95% confidence level</u>.

a1-17 Carbon

$$(\bar{x} - \mu)_{actual} = 68.5\% - 68.8\% = -0.3\%$$

At the 95% confidence level.

$$(\bar{x} - \mu) = \pm z\sigma/\sqrt{N} = \pm(1.96)(0.004 \times 68.8\%)/\sqrt{2} = \pm 0.38\%$$

<u>No determinate error is demonstrated</u>.

Hydrogen

$$(\bar{x} - \mu)_{\text{actual}} = 4.882\% - 4.953\% = 0.071\%$$

At the 95% confidence level,

$$(\bar{x} - \mu) = \pm 1.96 (0.006 \times 4.95\%)/\sqrt{2} = \pm 0.041\%$$

<u>Determinate error suggested</u>.

a1-18
$$V = \frac{4}{3}\pi r^3 = \frac{1}{6}\pi d^3 = \frac{1}{6}\pi (2.15 \text{ cm})^3 = \underline{\underline{5.20 \text{ cm}^3}}$$

$$s_d = 0.020 \text{ cm}$$

$$\frac{s_v}{V} = 3 \times \frac{s_d}{d} = 3 \times \frac{0.020}{2.15} \quad (\text{Equation 3, Table a1} - 5)$$

$$s_v = 5.20 \times 3 \times 0.020/2.15 = \underline{0.15 \text{ cm}^3}$$

a1-19 At pH = 2.00 (± 0.01)

$$x = [H_3O^+] = \text{antilog}(-2.00) = 1.00 \times 10^{-2}$$

$$\frac{s_x}{x} = \frac{s_x}{1.00 \times 10^{-2}} = 2.303 s_p \quad (\text{Equation 5, Table a1} - 5)$$

$$s_x = 1.00 \times 10^{-2} \times 2.303 \times 0.01 = \underline{\underline{2.3 \times 10^{-4}}}$$

Similarly at pH = 12.0

$$s_x = 1.00 \times 10^{-12} \times 2.303 \times 0.01 = \underline{\underline{2.3 \times 10^{-14}}}$$

a1-20
$$c = \frac{5.0000 \text{ g} (\pm 0.00002 \text{ g})}{100.00 \text{ mL} (\pm 0.15 \text{ mL})} = 0.05000 \frac{\text{g}}{\text{mL}}$$

$$\frac{s_c}{c} = \sqrt{\left(\frac{0.00002}{5.0000}\right)^2 + \left(\frac{0.15}{100.00}\right)^2} = \pm 1.5 \times 10^{-3}$$

$$s_c = \pm 0.05000 (\text{g/mL}) \times 1.5 \times 10^{-3} = \underline{\underline{\pm 7.5 \times 10^{-5} \text{ g/mL}}}$$

a1-21 (a) $s_x = 0.434 s_p / p \quad (\text{Equation 4, Table a1} - 5)$

$$= \pm 0.434 \times 4/878 = \pm 0.0020$$

$$x = \underline{2.943 (\pm 0.0020)}$$

(b) s_x = $0.434 \times (\pm 0.0004)/0.4957$ = $\pm 3.5 \times 10^{-4}$

x = $\underline{\underline{-0.3048 \, (\pm 0.0004)}}$

(c) Rewriting Equation 5 in Table a1-5 gives

$$\frac{s_p}{p} = 2.303 \, s_x = 2.303 \times (\pm 0.01) = \pm 0.02303$$

$$s_p = \pm 0.0203 \times 4365 = \pm 1.0 \times 10^2$$

$$p = \underline{\underline{4.4 \, (\pm 0.1) \times 10^3}}$$

(d) $\frac{s_p}{p}$ = $2.303 \times (\pm 0.002)$ = ± 0.0046

$$s_p = 6.44 \times 10^{-8} \times (\pm 0.0046) = \pm 0.03 \times 10^{-8}$$

$$p = \underline{\underline{6.44 \, (\pm 0.03) \times 10^{-8}}}$$

a1-22 (a) See broken line in the figure below.

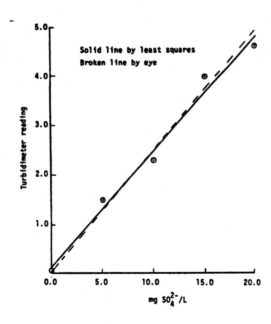

159

(b) See Section a1-C, page A-18.

x_i	y_i	x_i^2	y_i^2	$x_i y_i$
mg SO_4^{2-}/L	Reading			
0.00	0.06	0.00	0.0036	0.00
5.00	1.48	25.00	2.1904	7.40
10.00	2.28	100.00	5.1984	22.80
15.00	3.98	225.00	15.8404	59.70
20.00	4.61	400.00	21.1521	92.20
$\sum x_i = 50.00$	$\sum y_i = 12.41$	$\sum x_i^2 = 750.00$	$\sum y_i^2 = 44.4849$	$\sum x_i y_i = 182.10$

$\bar{x} = 50.00/5 = 10.00 \qquad \bar{y} = 12.41/5 = 2.482$

$S_{xx} = \sum x_i^2 - (\sum x_i)^2/n = 750.00 - (50.00)^2/5 = 250.00$ (Equation a1 − 29)

$S_{yy} = \sum y_i^2 - (\sum y_i)^2/n = 44.4849 - (12.41)^2/5 = 13.68328$ (Equation a1 − 30)

$S_{xy} = \sum x_i y_i - (\sum x_i \sum y_i)/n = 182.10 - 50.00 \times 12.41/5 = 58.00$ (Equation a1 − 31)

$m = S_{xy}/S_{xx} = 58.00/250.00 = 0.2320$ (Equation a1 − 32)

$b = \bar{y} - m\bar{x} = 2.482 - 0.2320 \times 10.00 = 0.162$ (Equation a1 − 33)

Letting c_x = conc of SO_4^{2-} = x_i

R = meter reading = y_i

$\underline{\underline{R = 0.232 c_x + 0.162}}$

(c) See the solid line in the figure in part (a).

(d)

$s_r = \sqrt{\dfrac{S_{yy} - m^2 S_{xx}}{N - 2}} = \sqrt{\dfrac{13.68328 - (0.232)^2 \times 250}{5 - 2}}$ (Equation a1 − 34)

$= 0.275 = 0.28$

$s_m = s_r/\sqrt{S_{xx}} = 0.275/\sqrt{250} = \underline{0.017}$ (Equation a1 − 35)

$s_b = s_y \sqrt{\dfrac{1}{N - (\sum x_i)^2/\sum x_i^2}}$ (Equation a1 − 36)

$= 0.275 \sqrt{\dfrac{1}{5 - [(50.00)^2/750]}} = \underline{\underline{0.21}}$

(e) $3.67 = 0.232c_x + 0.162$

$c_x = (3.67 - 0.162)/0.232 = 15.1 \text{ mg SO}_4^{2-}/\text{L}$

$$s_c = \frac{s_r}{m}\sqrt{\frac{1}{L} + \frac{1}{N} + \frac{(\bar{y}_c - \bar{y})^2}{m^2 S_{xx}}}$$

$$= \frac{0.275}{0.232}\sqrt{\frac{1}{1} + \frac{1}{5} + \frac{(3.67 - 2.482)^2}{(0.232)^2 \times 250}} = \underline{\underline{1.4 \text{ mg SO}_4^{2-}/\text{L}}}$$

Thus $c_x = \underline{\underline{15 \, (\pm 1) \text{ mg SO}_4^{2-}/\text{L}}}$

$\text{CV} = 1.4 \times 100/15.1 = \underline{\underline{9.3\%}}$

(f) Substituting $L = 6$ in the equation in part (e) gives

$c_x = \underline{\underline{15.1 \, (\pm 0.8) \text{ mg SO}_4^{2-}/\text{L}}}$

$\text{CV} = \underline{\underline{5.4\%}}$

a1-23 Proceeding in the same way as in Problem a1-22, we obtain

(a) See the broken line in the figure below.

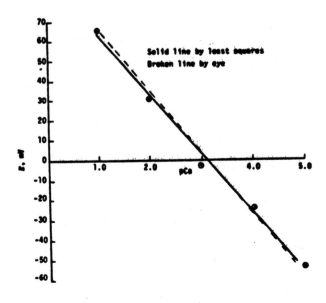

(b) $S_{xx} = \sum x_i^2 - (\sum x_i)^2 / n = 55.00 - (15.00)^2 / 5 = 10.00$

$S_{yy} = \sum y_i^2 - (\sum y_i)^2 / n = 8924.64 - (18.20)^2 / 5 = 8858.392$

$S_{xy} = \sum x_i y_i - (\sum x_i \sum y_i) / n = -242.8 - 15.00 \times 18.20 / 5 = -297.40$

$m = S_{xy} / S_{xx} = -297.4 / 10.00 = -29.74$

$b = \bar{y} - m\bar{x} = 18.20 / 5 - (-29.74 \times 15.00 / 5) = 92.86$

$y = mx + b$ and $\underline{E^0 = -29.74\,pCA + 92.86}$

See solid line in the figure in part (a).

(c)
$$s_r = \sqrt{\frac{8858.392 - (-29.74)^2 \times 10.00}{5 - 2}} = 2.138$$

$$s_m = \sqrt{(2.138)^2 / 10.00} = 0.676 = \underline{0.68}$$

$$s_b = 2.138 \sqrt{\frac{1}{5 - (15.00)^2 / 55.00}} = \underline{2.24}$$

(d) Substituting into the derived equation gives

$20.3 = -29.74\,pCA$

$pCa = (20.3 - 92.86) / (-29.74) = 2.440 = \underline{2.44}$

$$s_c = \frac{2.138}{-29.74} \sqrt{\frac{1}{1} + \frac{1}{5} + \frac{(20.3 - 18.20/5)^2}{(-29.74)^2 \times 10.00}} = \underline{0.080}$$

$CV = 0.080 \times 100 / 2.44 = \underline{3.3\%}$

(e) Using $L = 2$ and $L = 8$ in the denominator in the first term in the square root expression in the equation in part (d), we obtain

$s_c = \underline{0.061}$ $CV = \underline{2.5\%}$

$s_c = \underline{0.043}$ $CV = \underline{1.8\%}$

(f) $[Ca^{2+}] = $ antilog $(-2.440) = \underline{3.63 \times 10^{-3}}$

(g) Applying Equation 5 Table a1-5, we write

$$\frac{s_x}{x} = 2.303\,s_c$$

where s_x is the standard deviation for $[Ca^{2+}]$, $x = 3.63 \times 10^{-3}$ and s_c is 0.061 for the mean of 2 measurements and 0.048 for the mean of 8 measurements.

For mean of 2,

$$s_x = 3.63 \times 10^{-3} \times 2.303 \times 0.061 = \underline{\underline{5.1 \times 10^{-4}}}$$

$$RSD = 5.1 \times 10^{-4} \times 100/3.63 \times 10^{-3} = \underline{\underline{14\%}}$$

For mean of 8,

$$s_x = 3.63 \times 10^{-3} \times 2.303 \times 0.043 = \underline{\underline{3.6 \times 10^{-4}}}$$

$$RSD = 3.6 \times 10^{-4} \times 100/3.63 \times 10^{-3} = \underline{\underline{9.9\%}}$$

a1-24 Proceeding as in the solution to Problem a1-22, we find

(a) $\sum x_i = 18.00 \qquad \sum y_i = 105.67 \qquad \sum x_i^2 = 71.50$

$\sum y_i^2 = 2404.6103 \qquad \sum x_i y_i = 414.488$

$S_{xx} = 71.50 - (18.0)^2/6 = 17.50$

$S_{yy} = 2404.6103 - (105.67)^2/6 = 543.585483$

$S_{xy} = 414.485 - 18.0 \times 105.67/6 = 97.475$

$m = 97.475/17.50 = 5.570$

$b = 105.67/6 - 5.570 \times 18.0/6 = 0.9017$

Letting A = relative area and c_x = mmol/L of MVK

$$A = 5.57 c_x + 0.902$$

(b) Solid line in the figure below is the least-squares line. The experimental data points are within the circles.

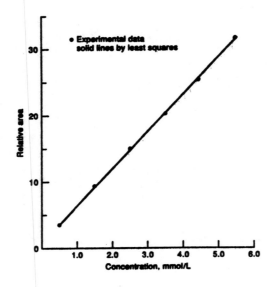

(c)

$$s_y = \sqrt{\frac{543.585483 - (5.570)^2 \times 17.50}{6-2}} = 0.403 = 0.40$$

$$s_m = \sqrt{(0.403)^2 / 17.50} = 0.0963 = \underline{\underline{0.096}}$$

$$s_b = 0.403 \sqrt{\frac{1}{6 - (18.00)^2 / 71.50}} = 0.333 = \underline{\underline{0.33}}$$

(d) For sample 1,

$$c_x = (6.3 - 0.902)/5.57 = \underline{\underline{0.969 \text{ mmol}/L}}$$

For sample 2,

$$c_x = (27.5 - 0.902)/5.57 = \underline{\underline{4.78 \text{ mmol}/L}}$$

(e) For sample 1, single measurement

$$s_c = \frac{0.403}{5.57} \sqrt{\frac{1}{1} + \frac{1}{6} + \frac{(6.3 - 105.67/6)^2}{(5.57)^2 \times 17.50}} = \underline{\underline{0.086}}$$

$$(s_c)_r = 0.086 \times 100/0.969 = \underline{\underline{8.9\%}}$$

164

For sample 1, for 4 measurements

$$s_c = \frac{0.403}{5.57} \sqrt{\frac{1}{4} + \frac{1}{6} + \frac{(6.3 - 105.67/6)^2}{(5.57)^2 \times 17.50}} = \underline{\underline{0.058}}$$

$$(s_c)_r = \underline{\underline{6.0\%}}$$

Proceeding in the same way for sample 2

For 1 measurement, $s_c = \underline{\underline{0.084}}$ and $(s_c)_r = \underline{\underline{1.8\%}}$

For 4 measurements, $s_c = \underline{\underline{0.056}}$ and $(s_c)_r = \underline{\underline{1.2\%}}$